ENCYCLOPEDIA OF
DINOSAURS
AND PREHISTORIC LIFE

ENCYCLOPEDIA OF
DINOSAURS
AND PREHISTORIC LIFE

Consulted by Steve Parker

Miles
Kelly

First published in 2017 by Miles Kelly Publishing Ltd
Harding's Barn, Bardfield End Green, Thaxted, Essex, CM6 3PX, UK

This edition printed 2018

2 4 6 8 10 9 7 5 3

Publishing Director Belinda Gallagher
Creative Director Jo Cowan
Editorial Director Rosie Neave
Senior Editor Claire Philip
Designers Helen Bracey, Joe Jones
Cover Design Jo Cowan, Rob Hale
Image Manager Liberty Newton
Indexer Marie Lorimer
Production Elizabeth Collins, Jennifer Brunwin-Jones
Reprographics Stephan Davis, Jennifer Cozens, Thom Allaway
Assets Lorraine King

Contributers Andrew Campbell, Dr Jim Flegg,
Rupert Matthews, Steve Parker

ISBN 978-1-78617-324-9

Printed in China

British Library Cataloguing-in-Publication Data
A catalogue record for this book is available from the British Library

Made with paper from a sustainable forest

www.mileskelly.net

Contents

Ancient life

Dinosaurs

Age of mammals

Humans

Ancient life

Prehistoric timescale

- **Earth's immense history is divided** into huge spans of time known as eras. These are drawn on a chart showing how long ago they occurred, in millions of years.

- **The main eras for living things** are Paleozoic or 'ancient life', Mesozoic or 'middle life', and Cenozoic or 'recent life'.

- **The eras are divided into periods**. For example the Mesozoic Era comprises the Triassic, Jurassic and Cretaceous Periods.

- **Each period is named after a feature** of the main rocks formed at that time. For example, the Jurassic Period is named after rocks from the Jura Mountains, part of the European Alps.

- **The last period**, the Quaternary, covers 2.6 mya to the present day. It includes the most recent group of ice ages, the last one being at its coldest just 21,000 years ago.

Quaternary Period 2.6–Present day

Mammoth: A type of elephant

Neogene Period 23–2.6 mya

Hyracotherium: An early horse

Paleogene Period 66–23 mya

Parasaurolophus: A duckbilled dinosaur

Cambrian Period
541–485 mya

Trilobite:
A shelled
marine creature

Ordovician Period
485–443 mya

Graptolite:
A simple
marine animal

Silurian Period 443–419 mya

Birkenia:
A type of fish

Devonian Period 419–359 mya

▶ ▼ Periods in Earth's prehistory.
The Cambrian to Permian make up
the Paleozoic Era ('ancient life'),
Triassic to Cretaceous make up the
Mesozoic Era ('middle life'), and the
Paleogene to Quaternary make up
the Cenozoic Era ('recent/new life').

Crinoid:
A simple marine
animal

Lepidodendron:
A primitive tree

Carboniferous Period 359–299 mya

Diplocaulus:
An early amphibian

Permian Period 299–252 mya

Rhamphorhynchus:
A winged reptile

Triassic Period 252–201 mya

Jurassic Period 201–145 mya

Cretaceous Period 145–66 mya

Stephanoceras:
A type of ammonite

Earliest plants

🦶 **Among the very first living things** on Earth were single-celled bacteria and cyanobacteria, also known as blue-green algae.

🦶 **Blue-green algae emerged** as long ago as 3500 mya. They contain chlorophyll and were the first living organisms to photosynthesize (make energy from sunlight).

🦶 **Photosynthesis** also produces oxygen. Over millions of years, the blue-green algae produced enough oxygen to enable more complex life forms to develop.

▲ *Lichens such as these are made up of an alga and a fungus. Early lichens – like modern-day ones – grew on rocks and, over time, eroded part of the rock and helped to form soil.*

▲ *Lichens can survive in many places where other plants would die, such as the Arctic, on mountaintops and in deserts. Some Arctic lichens are over 4000 years old.*

- **True algae**, which are usually regarded as plants, developed more than 1500 mya.

- **By about 550 mya**, multi-celled plants had begun to appear, including simple seaweeds.

- **Algae and lichens** were the first plants to appear on land.

- **Bryophytes** (mosses and liverworts) emerged on land by around 400 mya. They are simple green seedless plants.

- **Unlike vascular plants**, which emerged later, bryophytes cannot grow high above the ground because they do not have strengthened stems.

DID YOU KNOW?

Liverworts grew on mats of blue-green algae, which trapped nitrogen from the air. Liverworts used this nitrogen to grow.

Vascular plants

- **Vascular plants are more suited** to living on drier land than mosses and liverworts.

- **They have branching stems** with tube-like pipes (vascular bundles) that carry water and nutrients.

- **These stems and tubes** also mean the plants can stand tall. Early vascular plants had spores (reproductive cells, like seeds) – the taller the plant the more widely it can disperse its spores.

- **One of the first known** vascular plants was *Cooksonia*. It was about 5 cm tall, with a forked stem.

- **Scientists called palaeontologists** discovered fossil remains of *Cooksonia* in Wales. Palaeontologists study fossils of prehistoric plants and animals to see how they lived and evolved.

- **Rhynie in Scotland** is one site where lots of vascular plant fossils have been found.

- **The plants at Rhynie** would have grown on the sandy edges of pools in the Early Devonian Period (about 410 mya).

- **One plant fossil** found at Rhynie is *Aglaophyton*, which stood around 45 cm high.

- *Aglaophyton* had underground roots and tissues that supported the plant stem. It also had water-carrying tubes and stomata (tiny openings) that allowed air and water to pass through.

- **Land-living plants** were essential for providing conditions for animals to make the transition from the seas to land. They created soil, food and ground cover for shelter.

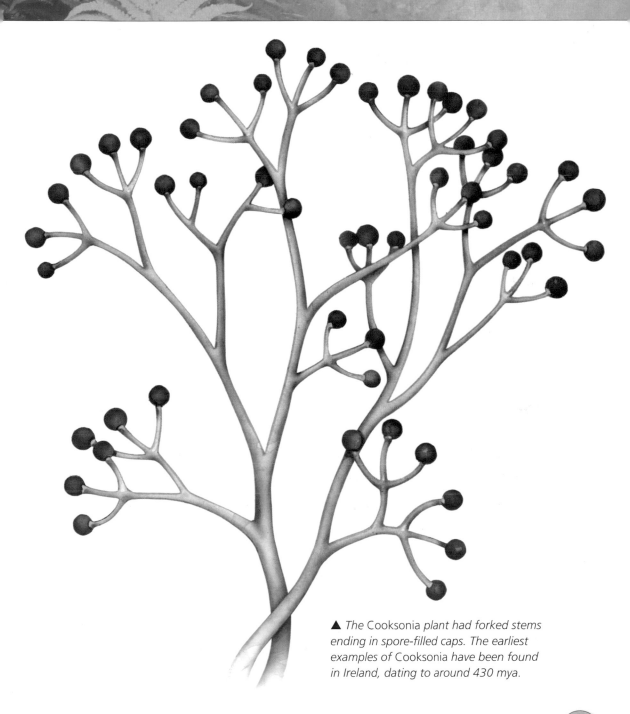

▲ The Cooksonia *plant had forked stems ending in spore-filled caps. The earliest examples of* Cooksonia *have been found in Ireland, dating to around 430 mya.*

Gymnosperms

- **Gymnosperms are plants** that produce exposed seeds on the surface of structures such as cones. The word gymnosperm comes from two Greek words: *gymnos*, meaning 'naked', and *sperma*, meaning 'seed'.

- **These plants** had appeared by 320 mya. They probably developed from early plants such as *Cooksonia*.

- **Gymnosperms** grew well in the damp, tropical forests of the Late Carboniferous Period (359–299 mya).

- **Varieties of gymnosperms** include conifers, cycads and seed-ferns.

- **Cycads are palm-like plants** with feathery tops. They were more common in prehistoric times than they are today.

▲ *Cycads have fern-like leaves growing in a circle around the end of the stem. New leaves sprout each year and last for several years.*

▶ *Also known as maidenhair trees, ginkgos are an ancient type of plant with fan-shaped leaves and fleshy yellow seeds.*

One type of cycad is the maidenhair tree, *Ginkgo biloba*. It still grows in towns and cities, but is now very rare in the wild.

One extinct gymnosperm is *Glossopteris*, which some palaeontologists believe was similar to the ancestors of later flowering plants.

Together with ferns and horsetails (a type of herb), gymnosperms dominated landscapes during the Mesozoic Era (252–66 mya).

▲ *Conifer trees have needle-like leaves and make their seeds in cones rather than in flowers.*

In the Jurassic Period (201–145 mya), plant-eating dinosaurs ate their way through huge areas of coniferous forest.

Today, conifers are found most often in cold or dry areas, to which they are well adapted.

▶ *This* Araucaria, *or monkey puzzle tree, is a type of conifer that dates back to the Jurassic Period.*

19

Angiosperms

 Angiosperms are flowering plants. They produce seeds within an ovary, which is contained within a flower. The word comes from the Greek terms *angeion*, meaning 'vessel', and *sperma*, meaning 'seed'.

 These plants first appeared about 140 mya.

The earliest evidence of flowering plants comes from the fossil remains of leaves and pollen grains.

Plant experts used to think that magnolias were one of the first angiosperms, but they now think that an extinct plant called *Archaefructus* was older. It lived about 125 mya.

 Fossil remains of *Archaefructus* were discovered in northeast China in the mid to late 1990s.

By 100 mya, angiosperms had developed into many dozens of families of flowering plants, most of which still survive today.

 By 60 mya, angiosperms had taken over from gymnosperms as the dominant plants on Earth.

The start of the Paleogene Period (around 66 mya) saw a rise in temperatures that produced the right conditions for tropical rainforests.

It was in the rainforests that angiosperms evolved into many different types of plants.

Angiosperms were successful because they could grow very quickly, they had very extensive root systems to anchor them and take up water and nutrients, and they could grow in a greater range of environments than other plants, such as gymnosperms.

▲ *An* Archaefructus *plant, which is one of the earliest known examples of an angiosperm. The* Archaefructus *fossil, which may be around 125 million years old, has a number of angiosperm features including enclosed seeds and flowers.*

21

The first invertebrates

- **An invertebrate is an animal** that does not have a spinal column. Invertebrates were the first animals to live on Earth, in the prehistoric seas.

- **The very first animal-like** organisms that fed on other organisms or organic matter were single-celled and sometimes called protists (protozoans).

- **Only prehistoric protists** with hard parts survive as fossils. The earliest fossils are more than 600 million years old.

- **One of the earliest known fossils** that could be a multi-celled animal is around 600 million years old. Called *Mawsonites*, it may have been a primitive jellyfish or worm – or the remains of a burrow or colony of microbes.

- **Some early invertebrate fossils** are from now-extinct groups of animals.

- **Some of these animals** had segmented bodies that looked a bit like quilts.

- **One such invertebrate** is *Spriggina*, named after geologist Reg Sprigg. In 1946, he discovered 550-million-year-old fossil remains near Ediacara in southern Australia.

- **Palaeontologists** have unearthed the fossils of many other invertebrates that resemble jellyfish from Ediacara.

DID YOU KNOW?

Spriggina has a curved, shield-like end to one part of its body. Some palaeontologists think this was its head, while others think it was an anchor that secured it to the seabed.

Another famous invertebrate discovery was made by Roger Mason, an English schoolboy, in 1957. This was the fossil of *Charnia*, an animal that was similar to a living sea pen.

▼ Charnia *was a prehistoric animal that grew in feather-like colonies attached to the seabed, like living sea pens.* Charnia *fossils date to more than 500 mya.*

Arthropods

- **Arthropods form** the largest single group of animals. They include insects, crustaceans (crabs and lobsters), arachnids (spiders) and myriapods (millipedes) – any creature with a segmented body and jointed limbs.

- **Some of the earliest known remains** of arthropods come from the 505-million-year-old mudstone deposits of the Burgess Shale in Canada.

- *Marrella* **is one of the most common fossils** discovered at the Burgess Shale. It was about 2 cm long and had a head shield and two antennae.

- **Its body was divided** into segments, each of which had a jointed limb, probably for scurrying over the seabed.

- **At first**, palaeontologists thought *Marrella* was a trilobite, but they now regard it as an entirely different type of arthropod.

- **One of the first** – if not the first – groups of animals to emerge from the sea and colonize the land were arthropods, some time between 500 and 400 mya.

- **Arthropods were well suited** for living on land. Many had exoskeletons (outer skeletons) that prevented them from drying out. Their jointed limbs meant they could move over the ground.

- **Woodlice-like creatures** may have been among the first arthropods on land. They fed on rotting plant material, which they would have found on seashores.

- **The largest-ever land arthropod** was a millipede-like creature called *Arthropleura*, which was 1.8 m long.

- *Arthropleura* **lived on forest floors** during the Carboniferous Period (359–299 mya). Like woodlice, it ate rotting plants.

◄ Arthropleura *was as long as a human. It was the biggest-ever land arthropod – a group of creatures that were the first to colonize the land.*

Molluscs and graptolites

- **Modern molluscs** include gastropods (slugs, snails and limpets), bivalves (clams, oysters, mussels and cockles) and cephalopods (octopuses, squids and cuttlefish).

- **Modern and prehistoric molluscs** represent one of the most diverse animal groups ever to have lived.

- **The first molluscs** were the size of a pinhead. They appeared early in the Cambrian Period, about 540 mya, or even before.

- **The first cephalopod molluscs** emerged towards the end of the Cambrian Period, around 490 mya.

- **One early cephalopod** was *Plectronoceras*, which had a horn-shaped shell divided into different chambers.

- **Gastropod molluscs** (snails and slugs) were one of the first groups of animals to live on land.

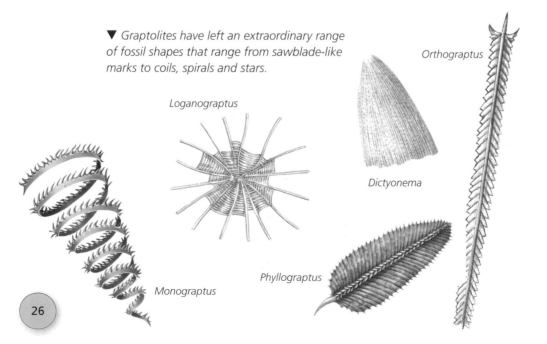

▼ *Graptolites have left an extraordinary range of fossil shapes that range from sawblade-like marks to coils, spirals and stars.*

Loganograptus

Orthograptus

Dictyonema

Monograptus

Phyllograptus

▲ *Nautiloids such as* Orthoceratites *had a long shells and squid-like tentacles, shown here hunting on the seabed almost half a billion years ago.*

Snails and slugs are limited to where they can live on land as they require moist conditions.

Cephalopods are the most highly developed of all molluscs. Squids and octopuses evolved big brains, good eyesight, tentacles and beak-like jaws.

Graptolites are an extinct group of simple animals that lived in string-like communities. Graptolite means 'written stone' because the fossils of these creatures resemble scrawled handwriting.

Graptolites had tentacles that they may have used to sieve food particles from the water or the seabed.

27

Ammonites

- **Ammonites belong to** the cephalopod group of molluscs. They were once widespread in the oceans, but they died out at the end of the Cretaceous Period (about 66 mya).

- **The number of ammonite fossils** that have been found shows how plentiful these animals once were.

- **Ammonites were predators** and scavengers. They had very good vision, long seizing tentacles and powerful mouths.

- **Their mouths consisted** of sharp beaks, perhaps venom glands, and a tooth-covered tongue.

- **Ammonites had multi-chambered shells** that contained gas and worked like flotation tanks, keeping the creatures afloat.

- *Stephanoceras* **was an ammonite** with a spiral, disc-shaped shell, 20 cm across. It was very common in the seas of the Mesozoic Era.

- **A living relative** of ammonites is *Nautilus*, a cephalopod that lives near the seabed and feeds on small creatures and carrion.

Chambers

▶ A rock containing an ammonite fossil, clearly displaying the shell's division into different chambers. The innermost chamber was the home of a newborn ammonite. As it grew, it built a bigger chamber and moved into it. When it outgrew that chamber it built another one, and so on, to form a spiral-patterned shell.

People once thought that ammonite fossils were the fossils of curled-up snakes.

 Builders have traditionally set ammonite fossils into the walls of buildings for decoration.

▼ *An ammonite swims through the sea in search of food. The animal swam backwards, with its tentacles trailing behind.*

29

Trilobites

Trilobites belonged to the invertebrate group called arthropods – animals with segmented bodies and hard outer skeletons.

The name trilobite means 'three lobes'. Trilobites' hard outer shells were divided into three parts.

The first trilobites appeared by about 520 mya. By 500 mya, they had developed into many different types.

These invertebrates had compound eyes, like insects' eyes, which could see in many different directions at once.

Some trilobites could roll up into a ball, like some woodlice do today. This was a useful means of protection.

Long, thin, jointed legs enabled trilobites to move quickly over the seabed or sediment covering it.

▲ Kolihapeltis, *from about 400 mya, had many long rear-pointing spines.*

◀ Trinucleus *was hardly larger than a thumb but had two very long swept-back head spines.*

Trilobites moulted by shedding their outer skeletons. Most trilobite fossils are the remains of these shed skeletons.

 One of the largest known trilobites was *Isotelus*, which grew more than 70 cm long.

 Other trilobites were much smaller, such as *Conocoryphe*, which was about 2–5 cm long.

 Trilobites became extinct around 250 mya – along with huge numbers of other marine animals.

▶ *This* Conocoryphe *trilobite lived in the seas of the Mid Cambrian Period, about 510 mya. It was one of the smaller trilobites.*

31

Pikaia

 A small, worm-like creature called *Pikaia* is thought to be similar to the ancestors of backboned animals.

 Its fossil remains were found in the 505-million-year-old mudstone deposits of the Burgess Shale in Canada.

 Pikaia **may have been** an early chordate, a group of animals with a stiff supporting rod, called a notochord, along their back. All vertebrates belong to this group, as well as marine animals called tunicates and acraniates.

 Pikaia **was 5 cm long** with what could be a notochord (stiffening rod) running along its body – a kind of primitive spine that gave its body flexibility.

 The notochord also allowed the animal's simple muscles to work against it, and the body organs to hang from it.

 Pikaia **was very similar** to *Branchiostoma*, a small, transparent modern-day creature that lives in sand at the bottom of the sea.

 As it lacked a bony skeleton, paired fins and jaws, *Pikaia* was not really a fish.

 Pikaia **was a more complex creature** than many other animals found in the Burgess Shale. It suggests that other complex creatures must have lived before it, from which it evolved.

The head of *Pikaia* was very primitive with a pair of tentacles, a mouth and a simple brain (a swelling of the nerve cord) for processing information.

 ***Pikaia* swam** in a zigzag fashion, similar to a sea snake.

▼ Pikaia *looked a little like an eel with tail fins. The stiff rod that ran along its body developed into the backbone in later animals.*

Jawless fish

The first fish probably appeared during the Late Cambrian Period, about 500 mya.

These fish had permanently gaping mouths – as they had no jaws they could not open and close their mouths.

Early fish were called agnathans, which means 'jawless'.

▼ *Early jawless fish such as* Hemicyclaspis *could swim much farther and quicker than most invertebrates. This meant they could more easily search for and move to new feeding areas.*

Agnathans ate by sieving plankton through their simple mouth opening, also perhaps scooping up small items such as algae, tiny animals and rotting flesh on the seabed.

Among the oldest complete agnathan fossils are *Arandaspis*, which comes from Australia and was found in 1959, and *Sacabambaspis*, which comes from Bolivia and other countries in South America, the fossils of which were discovered in the 1980s.

Hemicyclaspis was another agnathan. It was a flat fish with a broad head shield and a long tail.

Later jawless fish had more streamlined, rounder bodies and eyes at the front of their heads. This suggests they were not restricted to the seabed.

Most jawless fish died out by the end of the Devonian Period (around 360 mya).

Living agnathans include lampreys and hagfish, which have soft bodies and look like eels. Like their ancient relatives, they do not have jaws.

▶ *The hagfish is a scavenger and parasite, even burrowing into a living host to eat it from the inside.*

Jawed fish

 The first jawed fish probably emerged during the Silurian Period (443–419 mya).

An early group of jawed fish were acanthodians, from the Greek word *akantha*, meaning 'thorn' or 'spine'.

Jaws and teeth gave acanthodians a huge advantage over jawless fish – they could eat a greater variety of food and defend themselves more effectively.

Jaws and teeth allowed acanthodians to become predators.

Acanthodians' jaws evolved from structures called gill arches in the pharynx (throat), the tube from the mouth to the stomach.

Gill arches are bony rods and muscles that support the gills, the breathing organs of a fish.

As acanthodians developed jaws, they also developed teeth.

The earliest fish teeth were cone-like shapes along the jaw, made out of bone and coated with hard enamel.

The teeth of early acanthodians varied greatly. In some species they were sharp and spiky, in others they were like blades, while in others they resembled flat plates.

DID YOU KNOW?

Another difference between jawed and jawless fish was that jawed fish had a pair of nostrils, while jawless fish only had one.

▲ Climatius, a type of acanthodian or jawed fish, lived around 400 mya. Another name for acanthodians is 'spiny sharks' – although they were not sharks, many had spines on the edges of their fins.

Sharks

- **The earliest known shark fossils** are scales from rock layers of the late Silurian Period, about 420 mya.

- **Sharks belong to the group** known as cartilaginous fish, which also includes rays and skates. Their skeletons are made from cartilage, not bone.

- *Cladoselache* **was a prehistoric shark,** which could grow up to 2 m long.

- *Cladoselache* **appears** to have been quite similar to a modern shark – it had a streamlined body, a pair of dorsal (back) fins and triangular-shaped pectoral (front side) fins.

- **Early sharks hunted squid,** small fish and crustaceans.

- *Stethacanthus* was a prehistoric shark that looked nothing like a modern one. It had an anvil-shaped head projection covered in teeth.

DID YOU KNOW?

Prehistoric sharks' jaws were fixed to the side of their skull, while modern sharks' jaws hang beneath their braincase, which gives them a more powerful bite.

▶ This modern blue shark is a fast swimmer and a fierce hunter. The main features of sharks – from their tightly packed, needle-sharp teeth to their streamlined shape – have changed little over 400 million years.

- *Stethacanthus* **lived** in the Carboniferous Period (359–299 mya).

- **Sharks are at the top** of the food chain in modern seas, but this was not the case during the Devonian Period.

- **Other Devonian fish** were much larger than sharks. For example, *Dunkleosteus* grew to be up to 3.7 m long and would have been able to snap up any contemporary shark in a flash.

▼ Hybodus *was a blunt-headed prehistoric shark that lived between 250 and 100 mya in the time of the dinosaurs. It looked quite similar to modern sharks, but had very different jaws.*

Bony fish

- **Bony fish have internal skeletons** and external scales made of bone.

- **Fossil evidence shows** they first appeared during the Late Silurian Period, around 420 mya.

- **Bony fish evolved** into the most abundant and varied fish in the seas.

- **There are two types** of bony fish – ray-finned fish and lobe-finned fish.

- **There were plenty** of prehistoric lobe-finned fish, but only a few species survive today. They belong to one of two groups – lungfish or coelacanths.

- **Amphibians** – and ultimately reptiles and mammals – evolved from lobe-finned fish.

- **Ray-finned fish** were so-called because of the bony rays that supported their fins. Most early ray-finned fish were small, ranging in size from about 5–20 cm long.

- *Rhadinichthys* and *Cheirolepis* were two early ray-finned fish. They were small predators equipped with good swimming ability and snapping jaws.

- **Around 250 mya**, ray-finned fish lost many of the bony rays from their fins. The fins became more flexible and the fish became better swimmers.

- **New types of ray-finned fish**, called teleosts, also developed more symmetrical tails and thinner scales.

▼ This modern-day coelacanth is a direct descendant of the lobe-finned bony fish that lived 350 mya. Coelacanths were thought to be extinct until a fisherman caught one off the coast of South Africa in 1938.

From fins to limbs

- **The first land-dwelling**, backboned animals were called tetrapods. They needed legs to hold up their bodies so they could move around in search of water and food.

- **Tetrapods evolved** from lobe-finned fish, which had all the right body parts to develop arms and legs.

DID YOU KNOW?

Suitable fins were not the only feature that meant lobe-finned fish could evolve into land-dwelling animals. They also had lungs for breathing air.

- **The fossil skeleton** of the lobe-finned fish *Eusthenopteron* shows that the organization of bones in its front and rear fins was similar to the arrangement of limbs in tetrapods.

- *Eusthenopteron* **lived in** shallow waters. It could use its fins as primitive legs and move over land if the waters dried out.

- **Recent research suggests** that another lobe-finned fish, *Panderichthys*, could use its fins more effectively as limbs than *Eusthenopteron*. According to scientists, *Panderichthys* was more like a tetrapod than a fish.

- **The front fins** in lobe-finned fish connected to a shoulder girdle, while the rear fins connected to a hip girdle. These girdles connected to the backbone.

- **These hip and shoulder** connections meant that the limbs of future tetrapods were connected to a skeleton, which prevented the limbs from pressing against the inside of the body and damaging it.

The shoulder girdle of lobe-finned fish also connected to their heads. Tetrapods, however, developed heads that were separated from their shoulders and joined instead by a neck.

Necks were a great advantage to land-living animals. They could use them to bend down, to reach up, and to turn around to see in other directions.

▲ Eusthenopteron *using its fins to move out of the water.* Eusthenopteron, *which means 'good strong fin', was once thought to be the closest ancestor to tetrapods. However palaeontologists have recently discovered other fish, such as* Kenichthys, Tiktaalik, Gogonasus *and* Panderichthys, *that may have been even closer relatives.*

Breathing air

- **Fish breathe oxygen** in water through their gills. When a fish is out of the water, these gills collapse.

- **For creatures to adapt** to living on land, they had to develop air-breathing lungs.

- **Tetrapods were not the first creatures** to develop lungs – this step was taken by lobe-finned fish.

- **Lungfish are lobe-fins** that still exist today. They live in hot places and when rivers dry out, they bury themselves in mud and breathe through lungs.

- **Early tetrapods**, such as *Ichthyostega* and *Acanthostega*, had gills and lungs, suggesting they could breathe in both air and water.

- **Later tetrapods breathed** through gills when they were first born, but, like modern frogs and newts, their gills became smaller as they got older and were replaced by lungs.

- **Modern amphibians** also take in oxygen through their skin, which is soft and moist.

- **Early tetrapods** had tougher skin, so were unable to breathe through it.

- **Breathing through skin** limits an animal's size, which is why modern amphibians are much smaller than many of their prehistoric ancestors.

DID YOU KNOW?

Animals could only evolve to live on land due to plants producing oxygen over millions of years, which became part of Earth's atmosphere.

▼ Prehistoric lungfish had lungs as well as gills. Like these modern lungfish, they were able to breathe air if the pools or rivers they lived in dried out.

Acanthostega

▲ Acanthostega *may have evolved from lobe-finned fish similar to* Eusthenopteron *and* Panderichthys. *It shared a number of features with these fish, including a similar set of gills and lungs, as well as a tail fin and braincase.*

Acanthostega was an early tetrapod. It had a fish-like body, which suggests it spent most of its life in water.

 Fossil remains of *Acanthostega* were found in rock strata dating from the Late Devonian Period (around 365 mya).

 Acanthostega's body was about one metre long.

 This tetrapod had a wide tail that would have been useful for swimming but inconvenient for moving on land.

 Acanthostega's legs were well-developed, with eight toes on the front feet and perhaps seven on the rear ones.

 The number of toes on its feet surprised palaeontologists – they had previously thought all tetrapods had five toes.

 The legs and toes would have helped *Acanthostega* give its body a thrusting motion when it swam. They would also aid movement through plants at the bottom of rivers and lakes in search of prey.

 Acanthostega had a flattened skull and its eye sockets were placed close together on the top of its head.

 A complete but jumbled-up *Acanthostega* fossil was discovered in hard rock in Greenland. Palaeontologists had to work very carefully to prise the fossil from the rock.

Frogs and salamanders

 Modern amphibians, such as frogs, toads, salamanders and newts, all belong to the group called the lissamphibians.

Lissamphibians evolved later than the early tetrapods, probably during the Late Permian Period (260 mya).

Triadobatrachus **lived** in the Early Triassic Period in Madagascar, was 10 cm long and had a frog-like skull.

Compared to earlier amphibians, *Triadobatrachus* had a shortened back with fewer spinal bones and a shortened tail.

Evolution did not stop with *Triadobatrachus* – modern frogs have even fewer spinal bones and no tail.

Triadobatrachus' **hind legs** were roughly the same size as its front legs. Again, this is different to modern frogs, which have long hind legs for hopping.

 The first known salamanders lived in the Middle Jurassic Period (174–163 mya) in China, Mongolia and Kazakhstan. They were about 20 cm long with a broad skull.

DID YOU KNOW?

Andrias scheuchzeri was a salamander from the Miocene Epoch (23–5 mya). It was named after the Swiss scientist Johannes Scheuchzer, who discovered it in 1726.

More modern-looking frog and salamander fossils have been discovered in Messel, Germany. They date from the Early Eocene Epoch (around 50 mya).

 Some Messel frog fossils have their legs bent as if they were in mid-hop. There are even tadpole fossils from Messel.

▼ Triadobatrachus *was one of the earliest known frogs. Frogs and salamanders may be descendants of a group of amphibious temnospondyls known as dissorophids.*

First reptiles

- **Reptiles evolved** from amphibians during the Carboniferous Period (359–299 mya).

- **Unlike amphibians**, which usually live near and lay their eggs in water, reptiles are much more adapted for living on land.

- **Compared to amphibians**, reptiles had better limbs for walking, a more effective circulatory system for moving blood around their bodies, and bigger brains.

- **They also had more powerful** jaw muscles than amphibians and would have been better predators. Early reptiles ate millipedes, spiders and insects.

- **One of the earliest reptiles** was *Hylonomus,* a small creature that lived in the Late Carboniferous Period, 315–310 mya.

- *Hylonomus* **lived in forests** on the edges of lakes and rivers. Fossil remains of this reptile have been found inside the stumps of clubmoss trees.

- **Another early reptile** was *Paleothyris*. Like *Hylonomus*, it was about 20 cm long and had a smaller head than amphibians.

- **One animal that may represent** a staging post between reptiles and amphibians is *Westlothiana lizziae*, which was discovered in Scotland in the 1980s.

- *Westlothiana lizziae* lived in the Early Carboniferous Period (about 335 mya).

▲ Hylonomus, *meaning 'forest dweller', was one of the earliest reptiles. Fossil hunters discovered its remains in fossilized tree stumps at Joggins in Nova Scotia, Canada.*

 At first, palaeontologists thought that *Westlothiana lizziae* was the oldest reptile. However, its backbone, head and legs more closely resemble those of an amphibian.

Eggs

 Reptile eggs were a major evolutionary advance over amphibian eggs.

 Early amphibians, like modern ones, laid their eggs in water. This is because their eggs were covered in jelly (like modern frogspawn) and would dry out on land.

 Reptiles evolved eggs that were covered by a protective shell. This meant they could lay them on land and they would not dry out.

▲ *Frogs lay their eggs in water in jelly-like clumps called spawn.*

▲ *A female snake protecting her eggs. Eggs laid on land are easier to protect than those laid in water.*

Embryo

Yolk

Amniotic fluid

Shell

▶ *Reptiles broke the link between reproduction and water by laying hard-shelled eggs on land. This snake shell contains the developing young (embryo), a food store (yolk) and a protective liquid (amniotic fluid).*

One advantage of shelled eggs was that reptiles did not have to return to water to lay them.

Another advantage was that reptiles could hide their eggs on land. Eggs laid in water are easy pickings for hungry animals.

Reptile embryos complete all their growth phases inside eggs. When they hatch they look like miniature adults.

In contrast, baby amphibians hatch out of their eggs as larvae, such as tadpoles. They live in water and breathe through gills before they develop lungs and can live on land.

Reptile shells are hard and protect the growing embryos. The eggs also provide the embryos with food while they develop.

During the evolution from amphibians to reptiles, some tetrapods laid jelly-covered eggs on land.

A number of today's amphibians lay jelly-covered eggs on land, including some tropical frogs and mountain salamanders.

Skulls

- **The jaws of reptiles** are another feature that shows the evolutionary progression from amphibians.

- **Amphibian jaws** are designed to snap but not to bite together tightly.

- **In contrast**, reptiles had more jaw muscles and could press their jaws together more firmly. This meant they could break insect body casings and chew through tough plant stems.

- **By the Late Carboniferous Period** (about 300 mya), reptiles developed openings in their skulls behind the eye socket. These openings allowed room for more jaw muscles.

- **Four types of reptile skull** developed. Each belonged to a different type of reptile.

- **Anapsids had no openings** in their skull other than the eye sockets. Turtles and tortoises are anapsids.

- **Euryapsids had one opening** high up on either side of the skull. Sea reptiles such as ichthyosaurs and plesiosaurs were euryapsids, but this group has no surviving relatives.

- **Synapsids had one opening** low down on either side of the skull. Mammal-like reptiles and mammals are descended from this group.

- **Diapsids had two openings** on each side of the skull. Dinosaurs and pterosaurs were diapsids – so too are crocodiles, lizards, snakes and birds.

▼ Varanosaurus *was a one metre-long synapsid reptile that lived in North America in the Permian Period, about 280–260 mya. There are important similarities between the skulls of synapsid reptiles and mammals.*

Synapsids

 Synapsids were tetrapods that had one opening on each side of the lower skull behind the eye socket, onto which their jaw muscles attached.

 They appeared in the Late Carboniferous Period (about 310 mya), and became the dominant land animals in the Permian Period (299–252 mya).

 Synapsids are the ancestors of mammals, which explains why they are sometimes described as 'mammal-like reptiles'.

 The first synapsids are called pelycosaurs. They were large, heavy-bodied animals that walked a bit like modern-day crocodiles.

 The fierce meat-eater *Dimetrodon* and the plant-eating *Edaphosaurus* – both of which had long, fan-like spines on their backs – were pelycosaurs.

 Later synapsids are called therapsids. The earliest therapsids had bigger skulls and jaws than pelycosaurs, as well as longer legs and shorter tails.

 Later therapsids are divided into two subgroups – dicynodonts and cynodonts. Dicynodont means 'two dog teeth' – cynodont means 'dog tooth'.

 Dicynodonts were herbivores. Most had round, hippopotamus-shaped bodies, and beaks that they used to cut plant stems.

Cynodonts were carnivores. They used different teeth in their mouth for different tasks – for stabbing, nipping and chewing.

 Some cynodonts had whiskers and may even have been warm-blooded, like mammals.

▼ Diictodon *was a small mammal-like reptile that lived about 255 mya. A plant-eater and a burrower,* Diictodon *was an advanced form of a synapsid known as a dicynodont.*

Crocodilians

The broad group containing living and extinct crocodiles, Crocodylomorpha, appeared in the Late Permian Period, about 260–255 mya.

The first true crocodiles appeared during the Late Triassic Period (220–201 mya). They were called protosuchians and lived in pools and rivers.

As its name suggests, *Protosuchus* was a protosuchian. It had a short skull and sharp teeth, and would have looked quite like a modern crocodile.

Other early crocodiles, such as *Terrestrisuchus*, looked less like modern crocodiles.

Terrestrisuchus **had a short body** and long legs. Its name means 'land crocodile' because palaeontologists think it may have been more at home on land than in water.

The next group of crocodilians to evolve were the mesoeucrocodylians, which lived in the sea.

Metriorhynchus was a marine mesoeucrocodylian. It had flippers instead of limbs and very sharp teeth for stabbing fish. It lived in the Late Jurassic Period (around 160 mya).

The subgroup called eusuchians includes all modern crocodiles, alligators, gharials and caimans.

 Deinosuchus, **from 80–75 mya**, was thought to be the largest-ever crocodile at 11 m in length, until a recent discovery of more *Sarcosuchus* fossils.

▼ *Fossils of* Protosuchus, *meaning 'first crocodile', have been discovered in Arizona, dating to around 200 mya. Although* Protosuchus *was similar to living crocodiles in many ways, its legs were much longer.*

Turtles and tortoises

▲ Proganochelys, *an early relation of modern turtles and tortoises, had a 60-cm-long shell, but it was unable to pull its head or legs inside.*

- **Turtles and tortoises** both have shells that cover and protect their bodies. They belong to a group of reptiles called chelonians.

- **Chelonian shells** evolved from belly ribs that grew outside of the body.

- **The earliest chelonian fossils** come from the Mid Triassic Period (220 mya). They have been found in Germany and Thailand.

- **One very early chelonian** was *Proganochelys*.

- *Proganochelys* **had a well-developed**, heavily-armoured shell, but palaeontologists think that it could not pull its head, legs or tail inside it.

- **The ability to pull the head**, legs and tail inside the shell is important for turtles and tortoises because it provides them with maximum protection.

The protective shells of turtles and tortoises may have helped them survive at the end of the Cretaceous Period, 66 mya, when so many other reptiles became extinct.

 Tortoises have bigger shells than turtles. This is because they are very slow-moving land creatures – unlike the swimming turtles – and need more protection.

A huge number and variety of turtle fossils have been discovered at Riversleigh in Australia, dating from the Miocene Epoch (23–5 mya).

▼ Archelon *fossils show that, at 4 m long, it was similar to, but much bigger than, modern leatherback turtles. Its front limbs were thinner and longer than its hind ones and were more useful in the water.*

Snakes

 Snakes probably first appeared 120–110 mya. *Dinilysia*, found in Argentina and from the Late Cretaceous Period, lived about 80 mya.

 There are earlier snake-like fossils, but palaeontologists generally think these were snake-like lizards and not true snakes.

The ancestors of snakes were lizards. Palaeontologists think it would have been a varanid lizard, of which the modern monitor lizard is an example.

Snakes are an evolutionary triumph. They are one of the few land-living animals to survive and flourish without limbs.

Compared to other reptiles, snake fossils are rare. This is because snake bones are delicate and do not fossilize well.

Snakes evolved into a huge variety of types from the Paleogene Period (66–23 mya). Today, there are more than 3400 snake species living in nearly every type of habitat.

The 50 million-year-old fossils from Messel, Germany, include the well-preserved remains of a 2-m-long early python called *Palaeopython*.

Early snakes killed their prey by squeezing it to death. Modern boas and pythons also use this method to kill.

Poisonous snakes, such as vipers, adders and cobras, did not evolve until the Miocene Epoch (23–5 mya).

▶ Titanoboa *was the biggest known snake, up to 14 m long and weighing perhaps 1.2 tonnes. It lived in tropical forests around 60 mya in Colombia, South America, and may have hunted in water like today's bulkiest snake, the anaconda.*

DID YOU KNOW?

Snakes are one of the few reptile groups that had their main evolutionary development after the time of the dinosaurs.

Placodonts

 After adapting so well to life on land, some groups of reptiles evolved into water-dwelling creatures.

 Placodonts were early aquatic (water-living) reptiles. They lived during the Triassic Period (about 252–201 mya).

 The name placodont means 'plate tooth'. These reptiles had large cheek teeth that worked like crushing plates.

 Placodonts appeared at about the same time as another group of aquatic reptiles called nothosaurs.

 They had shorter, sturdier bodies than the nothosaurs but, like them, they did not survive as a group for long.

 Placodus **was a placodont**. It had a stocky body, stumpy limbs and webbed toes for paddling. It may have had a fin on its tail.

 Placodus **probably used** its wide, flat teeth, which pointed outwards from its mouth, to prise shellfish off rocks or the seabed.

 Psephoderma was a turtle-like placodont. Its body was covered by a bony shell, which was in turn covered by hard horny plates.

 Psephoderma **also had** a horny beak, like a turtle's, and paddle-shaped limbs.

 Henodus **was another** turtle-like placodont. It also had a beak, which it probably used to grab molluscs from the seabed.

▶ Placodus *grew up to 2 m long and probably used its sticking-out front teeth to scrape up molluscs from the seabed. Its plate-like side teeth would then make short work of crunching the molluscs.*

Nothosaurs

 Another group of reptiles that returned to live in the sea were the nothosaurs.

As its name implies, *Nothosaurus* was a nothosaur. Its neck, tail and body were long and flexible.

Nothosaurus **was about** 4 m long and its approximate weight was 250 kg.

Impressions left in some *Nothosaurus* fossils show that it had webs between its toes.

Nothosaurus' **jaw** had many sharp, interlocking teeth, which would have crunched up the fish and shrimps on which it fed.

Ceresiosaurus was another nothosaur. Palaeontologists think it swam by swaying its body and tail from side to side, like a fish.

Ceresiosaurus means 'lizard of Ceresio'. It was as long as *Nothosaurus* but slimmer, only 120 kg in weight.

Nothosaurs emerged near the start of the Triassic Period about 250 mya, but were extinct by the end of it.

 The place left by the extinct nothosaurs was taken by the plesiosaurs – another group of marine reptiles that were better adapted to life in the seas.

▲ Nothosaurus *was an aquatic reptile that could use its webbed feet to move over land. The long-necked nothosaurs were probably the ancestors of plesiosaurs, many of which also had long necks.*

67

Plesiosaurs

- **Plesiosaurs were marine reptiles** that were plentiful from the Late Triassic to the Late Cretaceous Periods (210–66 mya).

- **They were better suited** to a marine lifestyle than nothosaurs or placodonts. Their limbs were fully developed paddles, which propelled their short bodies quickly through the water.

- **Many plesiosaurs** had a long, bendy neck. They had small heads with strong jaws and sharp teeth.

- **These marine reptiles** had a diet that included fish, squid and probably pterosaurs (flying reptiles), which flew above the water in search of food.

- **The first *Plesiosaurus* fossil** was discovered at Lyme Regis on the south coast of England by Mary Anning in the early 19th century. The fossil, which is in the Natural History Museum, London, is 2.3 m long.

- ***Plesiosaurus* was not** a fast swimmer. It used its flipper-like limbs to move through the water but it had a weak tail that could not propel it forward very powerfully.

- ***Elasmosaurus***, the longest plesiosaur, lived late in the Cretaceous Period, about 80 mya. It grew up to 14 m long and weighed up to 3 tonnes.

● **One group of plesiosaurs** were known as pliosaurs. They had much shorter necks and much larger heads, with huge jaws and enormous teeth.

● **Research suggests** that plesiosaurs may have caught their prey with quick, darting head movements.

▲ *Long-necked* Elasmosaurus *was one of the last of the plesiosaurs. It lived in a shallow sea that covered much of North America about 80 mya.*

Ichthyosaurs

🐾 **Ichthyosaurs looked similar** to sharks, which are fish, and to later dolphins, which are mammals. When one type of animal comes to look like another, scientists call it convergent evolution.

🐾 **Unlike plesiosaurs**, which relied on their paddles to propel them forwards, ichthyosaurs swayed their tails from side to side like fish.

🐾 **Hundreds of complete skeletons** of the ichthyosaur *Ichthyosaurus* have been discovered. This reptile could grow up to 2 m long and weighed 90 kg.

🐾 *Ichthyosaurus* **had very large ear bones**. It may have been able to pick up underwater vibrations caused by prey.

🐾 **Some fossilized skeletons** of *Ichthyosaurus* and other ichthyosaurs were found with embryos inside. This shows that ichthyosaurs gave birth to live young, as opposed to laying eggs.

🐾 **One of the largest ichthyosaurs** was *Shastasaurus*, which was over 20 m long and weighed perhaps 25 tonnes.

🐾 **Ichthyosaurs were plentiful** in the Triassic and Jurassic Periods (252–145 mya), but became rarer in the Late Jurassic and Cretaceous Periods, dying out 66 mya.

🐾 **Ichthyosaur means** 'fish lizard'.

🐾 **Fossil hunters have found** ichthyosaur remains all over the world – in North and South America, Europe, Russia, India and Australia.

▼ Fossil marine reptiles such as Ichthyosaurus *created a sensation in the early 19th century, before dinosaurs were discovered. Ichthyosaurs had long, slim jaws to snap up fish and squid.*

Mosasaurs

- **Another group of large sea reptiles** was the mosasaurs. They appeared from about 140 mya at the time when ichthyosaurs were becoming less common.

- **Mosasaurs were diapsid reptiles** – a group that included dinosaurs and pterosaurs. Most other large sea reptiles belonged to another group – the euryapsids.

- **Unlike other** giant prehistoric sea reptiles, mosasaurs have living relatives. These include monitor lizards, such as the Komodo dragon.

- **The best known mosasaur** is *Mosasaurus*, which could grow up to 16 m long and 20 tonnes in weight.

- **The huge jaws of *Mosasaurus*** were lined with cone-shaped teeth, each of which had different cutting and crushing edges. They were the most advanced teeth of any marine reptile.

- **So distinctive** are *Mosasaurus* teeth that palaeontologists have identified its tooth marks on the fossils of other animals, in particular the giant turtle *Allopleuron*.

- **The jaws of a *Mosasaurus*** were discovered in a limestone mine in Maastricht, in the Netherlands, in the 1770s. The fossil disappeared in 1795 when the French invaded Maastricht, but later turned up in Paris.

- **At first, scientists thought** the jaws belonged either to a prehistoric whale or a crocodile, until they decided they were a giant lizard's.

▼ Mosasaurus *was a fast swimmer. It had an enormous tail and paddle-shaped limbs, which it probably used as rudders.*

Mosasaurus **means** 'lizard from the River Meuse' because it was discovered in Maastricht in the Netherlands, through which the River Meuse flows.

In 1998, more than 200 years after the discovery of the first *Mosasaurus* fossil, palaeontologists discovered the remains of another *Mosasaurus* in the same location – the St Pietersburg quarry in Maastricht.

Rhamphorhynchoids

 The earliest pterosaurs (flying reptiles) were the rhamphorhynchoids. They first appeared in the Mid–Late Triassic Period (around 230–220 mya).

Rhamphorhynchoids had long tails that ended in a diamond-shaped vane, like a rudder. Their tails gave them stability in flight, which meant they could soar and swoop effectively.

One of the first rhamphorhynchoids – and first flying vertebrates – was *Peteinosaurus*.

Well-preserved fossils of *Peteinosaurus* have been found near Cene, Bergamo in Italy.

They reveal *Peteinosaurus'* sharp, cone-like teeth and suggest it ate insects that it caught in the air.

In contrast, another early rhamphorhynchoid, *Eudimorphodon*, had fangs at the front of its mouth and smaller spiked ones behind. This suggests that it ate fish.

Dimorphodon was a later rhamphorhynchoid from the Early Jurassic Period (201–174 mya). It had a huge head that looked a bit like a puffin's.

Rhamphorhynchus was one of the later rhamphorhynchoids, appearing in the Late Jurassic Period (about 160 mya).

▼ Dimorphodon *had a wingspan of about 1.5 m and a body length of 1 m. Palaeontologists think that it lived and hunted along seashores and rivers.*

DID YOU KNOW?

Fossil hunters have found Rhamphorhynchus fossils alongside those of the early bird Archaeopteryx in Solnhofen, Germany.

Later pterosaurs

- **Pterodactyls are a later group** of pterosaurs (flying reptiles) than the rhamphorhynchoids.

- **They lived in the Late Jurassic** through to the Late Cretaceous Periods (about 160–66 mya).

- **Although pterodactyls** lacked the long, stabilizing tail of rhamphorhynchoids, they were probably more effective fliers and able to make quicker turns in the air.

- **These later pterosaurs** were also much lighter than rhamphorhynchoids because their bones were hollow.

- **The pterodactyl** *Pterodactylus* and the rhamphorhynchoid *Rhamphorhynchus* were roughly the same size, but *Pterodactylus* weighed between 1–5 kg, while *Rhamphorhynchus* was heavier at about 10 kg.

- **Some of the largest pterodactyls**, such as *Pteranodon*, appeared in the Late Cretaceous Period and had wingspans of over 5 m.

🐾 **Unlike earlier flying reptiles**, *Pteranodon* had no teeth. Instead, it used its long, thin beak to scoop up fish.

🐾 **At the bottom** of its mouth *Pteranodon* had a pelican-like pouch – it probably used this to store fish before swallowing them.

🐾 *Pteranodon* **weighed** over 20 kg. This was heavier than earlier pterodactyls and suggests it was probably a glider rather than an active flyer.

🐾 **A long crest** on *Pteranodon's* head may have worked as a rudder during flight.

◀ *The largest type of* Pteranodon *had a wingspan of more than 6 m. It lived about 88–80 million years ago, feeding on fish that lived in the shallow seas that then covered much of North America.*

Dinosaurs

Ancestors

- **Experts have many opinions** about which group (or groups) of reptiles were the ancestors of the dinosaurs.

- **Very early dinosaurs** walked and ran on their strong back limbs, so their ancestors probably did the same.

- **One group name** for the dinosaurs' ancestors was the thecodonts, or 'socket-toothed', but this is no longer regarded as a true scientific grouping.

- **However there are several kinds** of small, slim, bipedal (walking on back legs), sharp-toothed reptiles that could show what the dinosaurs' ancestors looked like.

- **Largerperton**, 70 cm long, lived about 240 mya in Argentina, South America.

- **Marasuchus** was a similar creature but even smaller, less than 50 cm in length, also from Argentina.

- **Lagosuchus** was another small predator about 30 cm long from the same area, although it may have been the same as *Marasuchus*.

- **Euparkeria** from South Africa dates from 235 mya, but its rear legs were not as well developed.

DID YOU KNOW?

The earliest known dinosaurs came from South America, so their ancestors probably did, too.

▶ Euparkeria, or 'Parker's good animal', was named in 1913. It was about 60 cm in total length, slim and agile, and resembled the creatures from which dinosaurs probably evolved.

Earliest dinosaurs

- **The first dinosaurs** had appeared about 230 mya, in the Middle Triassic Period.

- **These dinosaurs** were small-to-medium meat-eaters with sharp teeth and claws. They ran quickly on their two longer, stronger back legs.

- **Fossils of *Herrerasaurus*** date from 230 mya and were found near San Juan in Argentina, South America.

- ***Herrerasaurus* was about** 3–5 m in total length, and probably weighed some 200–250 kg.

- **Perhaps slightly earlier**, about 231 mya, and in the same place as *Herrerasaurus*, there lived a similar-shaped dinosaur named *Eoraptor*, which was only 1–1.5 m long and weighed 10 kg.

- **The name *Eoraptor*** means 'dawn plunderer' or 'early thief'.

- ***Staurikosaurus*** was a meat-eater similar to *Herrerasaurus*. It is known to have lived around 225 mya, in present-day Brazil, South America.

DID YOU KNOW?

Eoraptor and Herrerasaurus hunted small animals such as lizards, insects and lizard-like reptiles.

Procompsognathus was another early meat-eater. It lived 210 mya in the Late Triassic Period in Germany.

 Pisanosaurus lived in Argentina in the Late Triassic Period, and was only one metre long. It may have been a plant-eater.

▼ *The very early meat-eater* Herrerasaurus *dates to about 230 mya. The discovery of an almost complete skeleton in 1988 allowed a good reconstruction.*

Eodromaeus
and Eoraptor

- ***Eodromaeus* was another** of several small, bipedal (walking on two legs) dinosaurs from early in their time.

- **Its fossils were discovered** in Argentina in 1996, and at first they were thought to be from the similar *Eoraptor*.

- **More studies showed** they were a different dinosaur, which was named *Eodromaeus*, meaning 'dawn runner', in 2011.

- ***Eodromaeus* lived** about 230 mya during the early part of the Late Triassic Period, making it one of the earliest known dinosaurs.

- **It was quite small**, with a nose-tail length of 1.2 m. It was slim too, weighing 4–6 kg.

Its rear legs were much larger, longer and stronger than the front ones, which were more like arms.

 This body build indicates a fast, nimble creature that could dart and zigzag away from bigger predators.

 The top speed of *Eodromaeus* is estimated at anywhere between 25 and 40 km/h.

 Like *Eoraptor*, *Eodromaeus* probably snapped up small bugs, worms and little reptiles.

> ## DID YOU KNOW?
>
> Eoraptor had unusual leaf-like teeth at the front of its mouth. Towards the back of the mouth it had the more typical sharp, curving teeth of a meat-eater.

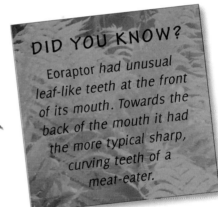

◀ *Eoraptor*, whose name means 'dawn thief', was similar in size to *Eodromaeus* at one metre from nose to tail-tip. It probably grabbed any small creature as prey.

Coelophysis

- *Coelophysis* **was a small, agile dinosaur** that lived early in the Age of Dinosaurs, about 220–200 mya.

- **A huge collection** of *Coelophysis* fossils was found in the 1940s, at a place called Ghost Ranch, New Mexico, USA.

- **Hundreds of** *Coelophysis* were preserved together at Ghost Ranch – possibly a herd that drowned in a flood.

- *Coelophysis* **was almost 3 m** in total length. Its slim, lightweight build meant that it probably weighed only 15–25 kg.

- *Coelophysis* **belonged** to the group of mostly meat-eating dinosaurs known as theropods. It probably ate small animals such as insects, worms and lizards.

- **Long, powerful back legs** allowed *Coelophysis* to run fast.

- **The front limbs** were like arms, each with a hand bearing three large, strong, sharp-clawed fingers to grab prey, and one small, non-functional finger.

86

- **The bird-like skull** was filled with small, sharp teeth.

- *Coelophysis* **means** 'hollow form'. It was so-named because some of its bones were hollow, like the bones of birds, making it lightly built.

▲ Coelophysis *would have stood almost waist-high to a person as it darted about on its long back legs.*

Dilophosaurus

 ***Dilophosaurus* was** a large meat-eating theropod dinosaur that lived about 195–190 mya.

Fossils of *Dilophosaurus* were found in Arizona, USA, and possibly other parts of the USA.

The fossils in Arizona were discovered by Jesse Williams, a Navajo Native American, in 1942.

Studying the fossils proved very difficult, and the dinosaur was not given its official name until 1970.

***Dilophosaurus* measured** about 6–7 m from its nose to the end of its very long tail.

The name *Dilophosaurus* means 'two ridged reptile', from the two thin, rounded, bony crests on its head, each shaped like half a dinner plate.

The crests were too thin and fragile to be used as weapons for head-butting.

Brightly coloured skin may have covered the head crests, as a visual display to rivals or enemies.

▼ Dilophosaurus *is one of the first big, powerful, predatory dinosaurs known from fossil evidence.*

DID YOU KNOW?

Dilophosaurus probably weighed over 500 kg – as much as the biggest polar bears today.

Eustreptospondylus

🦖 *Eustreptospondylus* **was a large meat-eater** that lived in present-day Oxfordshire and Buckinghamshire, in England. It lived about 165–160 mya.

🦖 **In the 1870s**, a fairly complete skeleton of a young *Eustreptospondylus* was found near Oxford, but was named as *Megalosaurus*, the only other big meat-eater known from the region.

🦖 **In 1964**, British fossil expert Alick Walker showed that the Oxford dinosaur was not *Megalosaurus*, and gave it a new name, *Eustreptospondylus*.

🦖 **A full-grown *Eustreptospondylus*** measured about 6 m in length and is estimated to have weighed over 400 kg, although the Oxford specimen was only part-grown.

🦖 **In its enormous mouth**, *Eustreptospondylus* had a great number of small, sharp teeth.

🦖 *Eustreptospondylus* may have hunted sauropods such as *Cetiosaurus* and stegosaurs, two groups of dinosaurs that roamed the region at the time.

DID YOU KNOW?

Eustreptospondylus means 'well-curved backbone'. This is due to the arrangement of its spine as seen in its fossils.

▼ *The fossils of* Eustreptospondylus *were found with those of sea creatures, suggesting it may have hunted along the seashore. This medium-sized theropod weighed about the same as two very large lions.*

Baryonyx

- *Baryonyx* **was a large meat-eating dinosaur** that lived about 130 mya.

- **The first fossil find** of *Baryonyx* was its huge thumb claw, discovered in Surrey, England, in 1983.

- **The total length** of *Baryonyx* was 9–10 m.

- *Baryonyx* **had a slim build** and a long, narrow tail, and probably weighed less than 2 tonnes.

● **The snout was unusual** for a meat-eating dinosaur because it was very long and narrow – similar to today's slim-snouted crocodiles.

● **The teeth were long** and slim, especially at the front of the mouth.

● **The general similarities** between *Baryonyx* and a crocodile suggest that *Baryonyx* may have been a fish-eater.

● **It may have lurked** in swamps or close to rivers, darting its head forward on its long, flexible neck to snatch fish.

● **The massive thumb claw**, which measured 35 cm in length, may have been used to hook fish or amphibians from the water.

● **The dinosaur was named** after this outsized feature – the name *Baryonyx* means 'heavy claw'.

◄ *Fossils of* Baryonyx *were found with the remains of fish scales, suggesting this dinosaur was a semi-aquatic fish catcher.*

Allosaurus

- **A big meat-eater**, *Allosaurus* was almost the same size as *Tyrannosaurus*. It lived about 155–150 mya, during the Late Jurassic Period.

- *Allosaurus* **was up to 11–12 m** in total length and its weight is variously estimated between 1.5 and 4 tonnes.

- **The head** was almost one metre in length, but its skull was light, with large gaps, or 'windows', that would have been covered by muscle and skin.

- **Not only could** *Allosaurus* open its jaws in a huge gape, it could also flex them so that the whole mouth became wider, for an even bigger bite.

- **Most** *Allosaurus* **fossils** come from the states in the American Midwest, especially Utah, Colorado and Wyoming.

- *Allosaurus* **may have hunted** giant sauropod dinosaurs such as *Diplodocus*, *Camarasaurus* and *Brachiosaurus*.

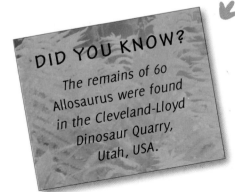

DID YOU KNOW?
The remains of 60 Allosaurus were found in the Cleveland-Lloyd Dinosaur Quarry, Utah, USA.

- **Fossils similar to** *Allosaurus* were identified in Europe and Africa, and a smaller 'dwarf' version was found in Australia.

▲ Allosaurus *almost rivalled* Tyrannosaurus *in size, but lived 90 million years earlier.*

Carnotaurus

- **The big, powerful, meat-eating** *Carnotaurus* belongs to the theropod dinosaur group. It lived about 75–70 mya.

- *Carnotaurus* **fossils** come mainly from the Chubut region of Argentina, South America.

- **A medium-sized dinosaur**, *Carnotaurus* was about 8–9 m in total length and weighed over one tonne.

- **The skull was relatively tall** from top to bottom and short from front to back, compared to other meat-eaters such as *Allosaurus* and *Tyrannosaurus*. This gave *Carnotaurus* a snub-snouted appearance.

- **The name** *Carnotaurus* means 'meat-eating bull', referring partly to its bull-like face.

- *Carnotaurus* **had** two cone-shaped bony crests, or 'horns', one above each eye.

- **Rows of extra-large scales**, like small lumps, ran along *Carnotaurus* from head to tail.

- **Like** *Tyrannosaurus*, *Carnotaurus* had small front limbs that could not reach its mouth and may have had no use.

- *Carnotaurus* **probably ate** plant-eating dinosaurs such as *Chubutisaurus*, although its teeth and jaws were not especially big or strong.

▶ The first, and so far only, fossil remains of Carnotaurus were discovered in 1984 and the dinosaur was named in 1985. It had small pebble-like scales embedded in its skin.

Yutyrannus

- **Named in 2012**, *Yutyrannus* or 'feathered tyrant' is a large predator dinosaur in the same group as the great *Tyrannosaurus*.

- **However, it lived** almost 60 million years earlier than *Tyrannosaurus*, about 125 mya, in what is now northwest China.

- *Yutyrannus* **was almost 9 m long** and could have weighed more than 1.5 tonnes.

- **It is the biggest dinosaur** so far that has feathers preserved with its fossil bones and teeth.

- **The feathers were slim**, flexible filaments, some more than 15 cm long.

- **Different specimens** of *Yutyrannus* have feathers on different parts of the body, so taking them all together, the filaments could have covered most of the dinosaur.

- **The skull of the largest** *Yutyrannus* specimen is almost one metre long.

It also has a small 'horn' above each eye, like several other tyrannosaur-group dinosaurs.

Like its relatives, *Yutyrannus* was a powerful predator with a huge mouth and many sharp teeth.

◄ Yutyrannus *lived in a region that was quite cool 125 mya, so its hair-like or plume-like feathers may have helped to control its body temperature.*

99

Tyrannosaurus

- *Tyrannosaurus* **is not only** one of the most famous dinosaurs, it is also one about which a great deal is known. Several discoveries have revealed fossilized bones, teeth and whole skeletons.

- *Tyrannosaurus* **lived** at the end of the Age of Dinosaurs, about 68–66 mya. It was 12 m long and weighed 7 tonnes.

- **Its full name** is *Tyrannosaurus rex*, which means 'king of the tyrant reptiles'.

- **The head** was 1.2 m long and had more than 50 dagger-like teeth, some longer than 15 cm.

- *Tyrannosaurus* **fossils** have been found at many sites in North America, including Alberta and Saskatchewan in Canada, and Colorado, Wyoming, Montana and New Mexico in the USA.

- **The arms and hands** of *Tyrannosaurus* were so small that they could not pass food to its mouth, and may have had no use at all.

- **Recent fossil finds** of a group of *Tyrannosaurus* include youngsters, suggesting that they may have lived as families in small herds or packs.

- *Tyrannosaurus* **may have been** an active hunter, pounding along with long strides after its fleeing prey, or it may have been a skulking scavenger that ambushed old and sickly victims.

- **Until the 1990s**, *Tyrannosaurus* was known as the biggest meat-eating dinosaur, and the biggest meat-eating animal ever to walk the Earth, but its size record was broken by *Giganotosaurus* and then *Spinosaurus*.

▼ Tyrannosaurus' *massive, powerful rear legs contrasted greatly with its puny front limbs or 'arms'. As it ran, its thick-based tail balanced its horizontal body and the head, which was held low. The rear feet were enormous, each set of three toes supporting some 3–4 tonnes.*

Carcharodontosaurus

- *Carcharodontosaurus* was one of the biggest meat-eating dinosaurs and land predators ever, rivalling *Tyrannosaurus* and similar types.

- **Some of its fossils** are very detailed, with the cavity inside the skull showing the shape of the dinosaur's brain, including the parts dealing with sight and smell.

- *Carcharodontosaurus'* teeth were about 20 cm long and triangular in shape.

- **The whole dinosaur** was about 13 m in total length and very powerfully built, with a weight of perhaps 10 tonnes.

- **Putting together** several specimen finds shows the skull was up to 1.7 m long.

- *Carcharodontosaurus* **lived** in North Africa about 100–95 mya, when the region had rivers, lakes, swamps and forests.

- **Its first fossils were dug up** in 1925, but more, larger specimens unearthed in the 1990s showed its true size.

- *Carcharodontosaurus* **belonged** to the group known as Carnosauria, which used to include all kinds of big meat-eaters but has recently been restricted to just a few kinds.

A cousin of *Carcharodontosaurus* may have been *Allosaurus* from North America, which lived about 50 million years before and was almost as large.

DID YOU KNOW?

Carcharodontosaurus was named 'ragged tooth reptile' after the great white shark, Carcharodon carcharias, due to similar jagged serrations along the tooth edges.

◀ Carcharodontosaurus was not the largest predator of its time and place, since the even greater Spinosaurus roamed the same region some 100 mya.

103

Giganotosaurus

- **In 1994** there was great news that remains of a meat-eating dinosaur even bigger than *Tyrannosaurus* had been found in Patagonia, in the south of Argentina.

- **The new find** was named as *Giganotosaurus*, 'giant southern lizard'.

- **The length of *Giganotosaurus*** was estimated at up to 13 m, and the weight between 8 and 10 tonnes.

- **The skull was at first said to be** 1.8 m in length, although this was then reduced to 1.6 m. It is still one of the most massive skulls of any dinosaur.

- **The remains of *Giganotosaurus*** were first noticed by Rubén Carolini, a local vehicle mechanic who went fossil-hunting in his spare time.

- **Its full name is *Giganotosaurus carolinii***, in honour of its discoverer.

- **Carolini went on to become** Director of the Villa El Chocón Municipal Museum, which celebrates his enormous find.

- **The main *Giganotosaurus* find** was an exceptional specimen, almost three-quarters complete.

- ***Giganotosaurus* lived** around 100–95 mya.

▲ Giganotosaurus *had three clawed fingers on each hand, and the hands and arms were not as undersized as those of* Tyrannosaurus.

 Not far away, the fossils of the colossal plant-eater *Argentinosaurus* were located, which lived around the same time – perhaps a victim of *Giganotosaurus*?

Spinosaurus

- **No other meat-eating dinosaur**, or any other land-based carnivore, found so far is as big as *Spinosaurus*.

- **This immense predator** has been known for over 100 years, but new finds in the 1990s and 2000s showed that it was the new record-holder.

- **The original *Spinosaurus* fossils** came from Egypt in 1912. They were named in 1915 by German palaeontologist Ernst von Stromer.

- **However those fossils**, kept in Munich Museum, Germany, were destroyed in 1944 by a World War II bombing raid. In 1996, 1998, 2000, 2002 and 2005, more fossils in North Africa were uncovered and identified as *Spinosaurus*.

- **This giant was probably** more than 14 m long and weighed over 9 tonnes, perhaps 15.

- **It had tall rods** of bone along its back called neural spines, that probably held up a sail-like area of skin, or perhaps a hump of flesh.

- ***Spinosaurus* and other finds** led to a new group of huge hunting dinosaurs being identified, the spinosaurs, which also included *Giganotosaurus*, *Carcharodontosaurus*, *Baryonyx*, *Oxalaia* and *Suchomimus*.

▶ *The skull and jaws of* Spinosaurus *were long and low, similar in shape to a crocodile and alligator and also to the medium-sized dinosaur* Baryonyx.

Ornitholestes

- *Ornitholestes* was a smallish meat-eater from the theropod dinosaur group.

- **The name** *Ornitholestes* means 'bird robber' – experts who studied its fossils in the early 1900s imagined it chasing and killing the earliest birds.

- **The home of** *Ornitholestes* was actually in present-day Wyoming in the USA – a continent away from the earliest birds in Europe.

- **Only one specimen** of *Ornitholestes* has been found. Parts of a hand at another site have been assigned to a different dinosaur.

- *Ornitholestes* **was** about 2 m long from nose to tail and probably weighed about 12–15 kg.

- **The teeth were small** and well-spaced, but also slim and sharp, well suited to grabbing small animals for food.

DID YOU KNOW?

According to some experts, Ornitholestes may have had a slight ridge or crest on its nose. Other experts disagree.

Ornitholestes **had very strong arms** and hands with powerful fingers and long claws – ideal for grabbing baby dinosaurs newly hatched from their eggs.

▼ Ornitholestes *relied on speed and its good senses of sight and smell for survival.*

Oviraptor

- *Oviraptor* **was an unusual meat-eater** from the theropod dinosaur group. It lived during the Late Cretaceous Period, about 75 mya.

- **Its fossils were found** in the Omnogov region of the Gobi Desert in Central Asia.

- **From beak to tail**, *Oviraptor* was about 2 m long.

- **It was named 'egg thief'** because its fossils were found lying among the broken eggs of what was thought to be the dinosaur *Protoceratops*. In fact they were probably the eggs of *Oviraptor* itself, the adult brooding or protecting them.

- *Oviraptor* **had no teeth**. Instead, it had a strong, curved beak, like that of a parrot or eagle.

- **On its forehead**, *Oviraptor* had a tall, rounded piece of bone, like a crest or helmet, sticking up in front of its eyes.

- *Oviraptor's* **head crest** resembled that of today's flightless bird, the cassowary.

- *Oviraptor* **may have eaten eggs**, or cracked open shellfish with its powerful beak.

DID YOU KNOW?
Oviraptor had two bony spikes inside its mouth that it may have used to crack eggs when it closed its jaws.

◀ Oviraptor's *unusual features* included its parrot-like beak. It may have been covered in filament-like feathers.

Smallest dinosaurs

▶ *About half of the length of*
Compsognathus *was its tail.*

 One of the smallest dinosaurs was
Compsognathus, which lived during the
Late Jurassic Period, 155–150 mya.

Its fossils come from Europe, especially
southern Germany and southeastern France.

Compsognathus **was probably** just over
one metre in length and may have weighed
less than 3 kg.

It had small, sharp, curved teeth and it probably
darted through the undergrowth after insects, spiders,
worms and similar small prey.

Discovered in 2004 in China, *Mei* was just 50 cm long. It is not
only one of the smallest dinosaurs ever found, it also has the
shortest dinosaur name of just three letters.

Mei **was fossilized** in a bird-like position with its head bent to one
side under its front limb or 'arm', just like a bird tucks its
head under its wing when asleep.

▶ *The tiny dinosaur Mei. Its full name,* Mei long, *means 'soundly sleeping dragon'.*

 The smallest fossil dinosaur specimens found to date are of *Mussaurus*, which means 'mouse reptile'. The fossils were of babies, just 20 cm long, newly hatched from eggs. The babies would have grown into adults measuring 3 m in length.

Two other small dinosaurs were the 60-cm-long *Caenagnathasia* and the 40-cm-long *Parvicursor*.

Pack hunters

🦶 **Dinosaurs were reptiles**, but no reptiles today hunt in packs in which members co-operate with each other.

🦶 **Certain types of crocodiles** and alligators come together to feed where prey is abundant, but they do not co-ordinate their attacks.

🦶 **Fossil evidence suggests** that several kinds of meat-eating dinosaurs hunted in groups or packs.

🦶 **Sometimes the fossils** of several individuals of the same type of dinosaur have been found in one place, suggesting the dinosaurs were pack animals.

🦶 **The fossil bones** of some plant-eating dinosaurs have been found with many tooth marks on them, apparently made by different-sized predators, which may have hunted in packs.

🦶 *Tyrannosaurus* may have been a pack hunter.

🦶 **At several North American sites**, the remains of several *Deinonychus* were found near the fossils of a much larger plant-eater named *Tenontosaurus*.

🦶 **One *Deinonychus*** probably would not have attacked a full-grown *Tenontosaurus*, but a group of three or four might have.

▼ *Small predatory dinosaurs such as* Troodon *may have gathered in groups to chase prey or scavenge.*

Raptors

- **'Raptors' is a nickname for** the dromaeosaur group. It is variously said to mean 'plunderer', 'thief' or 'hunter' (birds of prey are also called raptors).

- **Dromaeosaurs were** medium- to large-sized, powerful, agile, meat-eating dinosaurs that lived mainly about 110–66 mya.

- **Most dromaeosaurs** were 1.5–3 m from nose to tail, weighed 20–60 kg, and stood 1–2 m tall.

- *Velociraptor* **lived** 75–70 mya, in what is now the barren scrub and desert of Mongolia in Central Asia.

- **Like other raptors**, *Velociraptor* probably ran fast and could leap great distances on its powerful back legs.

- **The dromaeosaurs** are named after the 1.8-m-long *Dromaeosaurus* from North America – one of the least known of the group, from very few fossil finds.

DID YOU KNOW?

On each second toe, a dromaeosaur had a large, curved claw that it could swing in an arc to slash through its victim's flesh.

- **The most-studied raptor** is probably *Deinonychus*.

- **The large mouths** of dromaeosaurs opened wide and were equipped with many small, sharp, curved teeth.

◀ Velociraptor, *the 'speedy thief', was a typical dromaeosaur. Fossils of it were found in Central Asia. Most raptors probably had feathers, although for some there is no direct fossil evidence.*

Deinonychus

- *Deinonychus* **is one of** the best known raptors.

- **It thrived** in the Middle Cretaceous Period, about 115–105 mya.

- **Fossils of** *Deinonychus* come from the American Midwest, mainly from Montana and Wyoming.

- *Deinonychus* **was about 3–3.5 m** long from nose to tail and weighed 60–70 kg, about the same as an adult human.

- **When remains of** *Deinonychus* were dug up and studied in the 1960s, they exploded the myth that dinosaurs were slow, small-brained and stupid.

- **Powerful, speedy and agile**, *Deinonychus* may have hunted in packs, like today's lions and wolves.

- **It had large hands** with three powerful fingers, each tipped with a dangerous sharp claw.

- *Deinonychus* **also had** the massive, scythe-like claw, typical of the raptor group, on each second toe.

- **The tail was stiff** and could not be swished.

- *Deinonychus* **and other similar dromaeosaurs**, such as *Velociraptor*, were the basis for the cunning and terrifying raptors of the *Jurassic Park* films.

▶ *There is no direct fossil evidence for feathers in* Deinonychus, *but remains of many other raptor-type dinosaurs show feathers of various kinds, not for flight, but perhaps for insulation or display.*

Archaeopteryx

- **The earliest known bird** for which there is good fossil evidence, and which lived during the Age of Dinosaurs, is known as *Archaeopteryx*, meaning 'ancient wing'.

- *Archaeopteryx* **lived** in Europe during the Late Jurassic Period, about 150–147 mya.

- **At about 50–60 cm** from nose to tail, *Archaeopteryx* was about the size of a large crow.

- *Archaeopteryx* **resembled** a small, meat-eating dinosaur in many of its features, such as the teeth in its long, beak-like mouth, and its long, bony tail.

- **In 1951**, a fossilized part-skeleton was identified as a small dinosaur similar to *Compsognathus*, but in the 1970s it was re-studied and named *Archaeopteryx* – showing how similar the two creatures were.

- **Three clawed fingers** grew halfway along the front of each of *Archaeopteryx*'s wing-shaped front limbs.

- **The flying muscles** were anchored to its large breastbone.

- *Archaeopteryx* **probably flew**, but not as fast or as skillfully as today's birds.

DID YOU KNOW?

Archaeopteryx was covered with feathers that had the same detailed designs found in those covering flying birds today.

Clawed digits on
leading edge of
wing

Small teeth
in jaws

Strong rear legs
for running

Flight feathers suited
to agile manoeuvres
in the air

▶ Some reconstructions of
Archaeopteryx show feathers
only on the limbs and tail,
where they formed air-proof
flying surfaces. This bird could
probably glide, swoop and turn
as it pursued flying prey such
as dragonflies.

Long bony tail

121

Feathered dinosaurs

- **Fossils found** since the mid-1990s show that some dinosaurs may have been covered with feathers or fur.

- *Sinosauropteryx* **was a small**, one-metre-long meat-eater that lived 125–120 mya in China.

- **Fossils of** *Sinosauropteryx* show that parts of its body were covered not with the usual reptile scales, but with feathers instead.

- **The overall shape** of *Sinosauropteryx* shows that, despite being feathered, it could not fly.

- **The feathers may have been** for camouflage, for visual display, or to keep it warm – suggesting it was warm-blooded.

- **Fossils of** *Avimimus* come from China and Mongolia, and date from about 75–70 mya.

- **The fossil arm bones** have small ridges that are the same size and shape as the ridges on birds' wing bones, where feathers attach.

- **The 1.5-m-long** *Avimimus* had a mouth shaped like a bird's beak for pecking at food.

- **Most scientists today** believe that birds are descended from a group of small meat-eating dinosaurs called maniraptorans, such as *Troodon*.

If this is so, the modern way of classifying or grouping animals, called cladistics, means that birds are a subgroup of dinosaurs, not a separate group. That in turn means that dinosaurs are alive today – in the form of birds.

▲ Avimimus *may have evolved feathers for warmth, keeping cool, camouflage, display, to shield its eggs on the nest – or a combination of all these.*

123

Ostrich dinosaurs

- **'Ostrich dinosaurs'** is the common name of the ornithomimosaurs, because of their resemblance to today's largest bird – the flightless ostrich.

- **These dinosaurs** were tall and slim, with two long, powerful back legs for running fast.

- **The front limbs** were like strong arms, with grasping fingers tipped by sharp claws.

- **The eyes were large** and set high on the head.

- **The toothless mouth** was similar to the long, slim beak of a bird.

- **Ostrich dinosaurs** lived towards the end of the Cretaceous Period, about 100–66 mya, in North America and Asia.

- **Fossils of the ostrich dinosaur** *Struthiomimus* from Alberta, Canada, suggest it was almost 4 m in total length and stood about 2 m tall – the same height as a modern ostrich.

- **The ostrich dinosaur** *Gallimimus* was almost 8 m long and stood nearly 3 m high.

- **Ostrich dinosaurs** probably ate seeds, fruits and other plant material, as well as small animals such as worms and lizards, which they may have grasped with their powerful clawed hands.

- **Other ostrich dinosaurs** included *Dromiceiomimus*, at 3–4 m long, and the slightly bigger *Ornithomimus*.

▼ Ornithomimus *could reach speeds of perhaps 80 km/h when running. It had strong muscles in its hips and legs, enabling it to take long, quick strides.*

DID YOU KNOW?

Huge fossils of front limbs found in 1965, and named Deinocheirus, indicate a massive ostrich dinosaur 10 metres long, 4 m high and weighing up to 5 tonnes. No other remains have been discovered.

Herbivores

- **Hundreds of kinds of dinosaurs** were herbivores, or plant-eaters. As time passed, the plants available for them to eat evolved, and new dinosaurs became adapted to them.

- **Early in the Age of Dinosaurs**, during the Triassic Period, the main plants for dinosaurs to eat were conifer trees, ginkgoes, cycads and the smaller seed ferns, ferns, horsetails and club mosses.

- **A few cycads** are still found today. They resemble palm trees, with umbrella-like crowns of long green fronds on top of tall, unbranched, trunk-like stems.

DID YOU KNOW?

To maintain their huge bodies, sauropods probably had to eat for 20 hours a day.

- **In the Triassic Period**, only prosauropod dinosaurs were big enough or had necks long enough to reach tall cycad fronds or ginkgo leaves.

- **In the Jurassic Period**, tall conifers such as redwoods and araucarias or 'monkey puzzle' trees became common.

- **The huge, long-necked sauropods** of the Jurassic Period may have been able to reach high into tall conifer trees to rake off their needles.

- **In the Middle Cretaceous Period**, a new type of plant food appeared – the flowering plants.

- **By the end of the Cretaceous Period** there were many flowering trees and shrubs, such as magnolias, maples and walnuts.

These new plants meant that many new kinds of animals, including new herbivorous dinosaurs, evolved to eat them.

▼ *During the warm, damp Jurassic Period, plants grew in most areas, covering land that previously had been barren. Massive plant-eaters such as Barosaurus thrived on the fronds, needles and leaves of towering tree ferns, ginkgoes and conifers.*

Barosaurus was 26 m long and weighed 25–30 tonnes

127

Prosauropods

🦖 **The first big dinosaurs** were the prosauropods, also called plateosaurids. Most lived between 230 and 180 mya.

🦖 **They were plant-eaters**, with small heads, long necks and tails, wide bodies and four sturdy limbs.

🦖 **One of the first prosauropods** was *Plateosaurus*, which lived in Europe between about 215 and 205 mya.

🦖 *Plateosaurus* **walked on all fours**, but may have reared up on its back legs to reach leaves. It was up to 9 m long, and weighed as much as 3 tonnes.

🦖 **Another prosauropod** was *Riojasaurus*. Its fossils are about 220–215 million years old, and come from Argentina.

🦖 *Riojasaurus* **was 10 m long** and weighed about 2 tonnes.

🦖 **Over 20 fossil skeletons** of the prosauropod *Sellosaurus* have been found in Europe, dating from 215–210 mya.

DID YOU KNOW?

A similar and close relative to Riojasaurus was Melanorosaurus from Africa – South America and Africa were once joined together as part of Gondwana, 200 mya.

Lufengosaurus **was an early Jurassic prosauropod** from China, measuring up to 9 m in length. It was the first complete dinosaur skeleton to be restored in that country.

 The sauropods followed the prosauropods and were even bigger, but had the same basic body shape, with long necks and tails.

▼ Riojasaurus *was South America's first big dinosaur.*

129

Plateosaurus

- **The name *Plateosaurus*** means 'flat reptile', and the first kinds appeared around 215 mya.

- **Groups of *Plateosaurus*** have been found at various European sites, totalling more than 100 individuals.

- ***Plateosaurus* had jagged teeth** for chewing plants.

- **Its flexible, clawed fingers** may have been used to pull branches of food to its mouth.

- ***Plateosaurus* could bend** its fingers 'backwards', allowing it to walk on its hands and fingers, in the same posture as its feet and toes.

- **The thumbs** had large, sharp claws, perhaps used to jab and stab enemies.

- **Fossil experts once thought** that *Plateosaurus* dragged its tail as it walked.

- **Experts today think** that *Plateosaurus* carried its tail off the ground to balance its head, neck and the front part of its body.

- ***Plateosaurus* was one of the earliest dinosaurs** to be officially named, in 1837, even before the term 'dinosaur' had been invented.

▼ Plateosaurus *may have been able to reach leaves 2–3 m above the ground.*

Massospondylus

 ***Massospondylus* was a medium-sized** plant-eater belonging to the group known as the prosauropods.

 Africa and perhaps North America were home to *Massospondylus*, about 200–185 mya.

 In total, *Massospondylus* was about 4.5 m long, with almost half of this length being its tail.

 The rear legs of *Massospondylus* were bigger and stronger than its front legs, so it may have reared up to reach food high up.

 The name *Massospondylus* means 'huge backbone'.

Fossils of over 80 *Massospondylus* have been found, making it one of the best-studied dinosaurs.

***Massospondylus* had a tiny head** compared to its body, so it must have spent hours each day gathering enough food to survive.

🦶 **The front teeth** of *Massospondylus* were large and strong with ridged edges.

🦶 **The cheek teeth** were too small and weak to chew large amounts of food, so perhaps food was mashed in the dinosaur's stomach.

🦶 **In the 1980s**, some scientists suggested that *Massospondylus* was a meat-eater, partly due to its ridged front teeth, but this idea is now outdated.

▼ Massospondylus *probably spent most of its time eating to fuel its bulky body.*

DID YOU KNOW?

Massospondylus was named in 1854 by the anatomist and palaeontologist Richard Owen, who had invented the term 'dinosaur' about 12 years earlier. He thought at first the fossils came from three different reptiles.

Anchisaurus

- *Anchisaurus* **was** an early sauropod-like dinosaur.

- **Although officially named** as a dinosaur in 1885, *Anchisaurus* had in fact been discovered over 70 years earlier.

- *Anchisaurus* **was very small** and slim compared to other sauropods, with a body about the size of a large dog.

- **Fossils of *Anchisaurus*** date from the Early Jurassic Period, 200–190 mya.

- **The remains of *Anchisaurus*** were found in Connecticut and Massachusetts, eastern USA, and in southern Africa.

- **With its small, serrated teeth**, *Anchisaurus* probably bit off the soft leaves of low-growing plants.

- **To reach leaves** on higher branches, *Anchisaurus* may have been able to rear up on its back legs.

- *Anchisaurus* **had a large**, curved claw on each thumb.

- **The thumb claws** may have been used as hooks to pull leafy branches towards the mouth, or as weapons for lashing out at enemies and inflicting wounds.

DID YOU KNOW?

Remains of Anchisaurus or a similar plant-eater were the first fossils of a dinosaur to be discovered in North America in 1818.

▶ Anchisaurus *was about 2.2 m long. Its name means 'near lizard'.*

Biggest dinosaurs

- **Dinosaurs can be measured** by length and height, but 'biggest' usually means heaviest or bulkiest.

- **The sauropod dinosaurs** of the Late Jurassic and Early–Mid Cretaceous Periods were the biggest animals to walk on Earth, as far as we know.

- **However, today's whales**, and maybe the huge sea reptiles (pliosaurs) of the Dinosaur Age, rival them in size.

- **For any dinosaur**, enough fossils must be found for scientists to be sure it is a distinct type before they can give it a scientific name. They must also be able to estimate its size. With some giant dinosaurs, not enough fossils have been found.

- **Remains of *Supersaurus*** found in Colorado, USA, suggest a dinosaur similar to *Diplodocus*, but perhaps even longer, at 35 m.

- ***Diplodocus hallorum* fossils** found in 1991 in the USA may belong to a 35-m-long sauropod.

- ***Ultrasaurus* fossils** found in South Korea suggest a dinosaur similar to *Brachiosaurus*, but smaller. However these fossils are fragmentary and some experts disagree with their naming.

- ***Argentinosaurus***, from South America, is known from a few fossils, mainly backbones, found in the early 1990s. It may have weighed up to 100 tonnes.

▶ Seismosaurus *was named in 1991, but further studies in the 2000s show it was probably one of the species of* Diplodocus, *now known as* Diplodocus hallorum *or* Diplodocus longus.

Long neck for reaching high leaves

Sauropods

- **Sauropods were the biggest dinosaurs** of all. They lived mainly during the Jurassic Period, around 201–145 mya.

- **These huge plant-eaters** had tiny heads, very long necks and tails, huge, bulging bodies and massive legs, similar to those of an elephant, but much bigger.

- **Sauropods included** the well known *Mamenchisaurus*, *Cetiosaurus*, *Diplodocus*, *Brachiosaurus* and *Apatosaurus*.

- ***Rebbachisaurus* fossils** were found in Morocco, Tunisia and Algeria. It lived 100 mya.

- ***Cetiosaurus* was about** 15 m long and weighed 10–20 tonnes.

- **The first fossils** of *Cetiosaurus* were found in Oxfordshire, England, in the 1830s. It was the first sauropod to be given an official name, in 1841 – the year before the term 'dinosaur' was invented.

- ***Cetiosaurus*,** or 'whale reptile', was so-named because British fossil expert Richard Owen thought that its giant backbones came from a prehistoric whale.

DID YOU KNOW?

The name 'sauropod' means 'lizard/reptile foot'. It was given in 1878 by US fossil-hunter and dinosaur expert Othniel Charles Marsh, after the discovery of the famous Diplodocus.

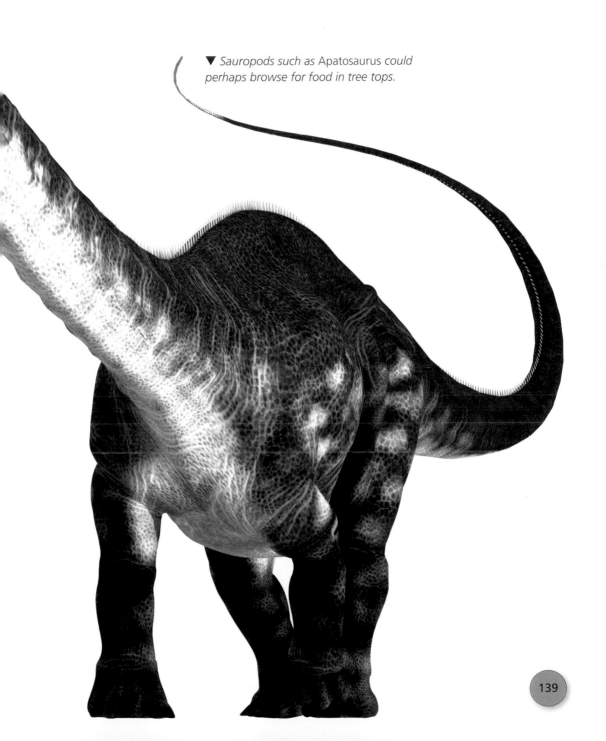

▼ *Sauropods such as Apatosaurus could perhaps browse for food in tree tops.*

Brachiosaurus

- *Brachiosaurus* **lived about 155–150 mya** and its fossils have been found at several sites in North America. Fossils of a similar dinosaur from Africa, previously thought to have been *Brachiosaurus*, have been renamed *Giraffatitan*.

- **At 25 m in length** from nose to tail, *Brachiosaurus* was not one of the longest dinosaurs, but it was one of the heaviest. Its weight has been estimated between 20 and 50 tonnes.

- *Brachiosaurus* **fossils** were first found in 1900 and the dinosaur was named the year after.

- **The name** *Brachiosaurus* means 'arm reptile' – it was so-named because of its massive front legs.

- **With its huge front legs** and long neck, *Brachiosaurus* could perhaps reach food more than 13 m from the ground.

Its teeth were small and chisel-shaped for snipping leaves from trees. The nostrils were positioned high on its head.

◀ Brachiosaurus *had similar body proportions to a giraffe, but was more than twice as tall and 50 times heavier.*

141

Camarasaurus

- *Camarasaurus* **was a giant plant-eating sauropod** that lived during the Late Jurassic Period, about 155–150 mya.

- **It is one of the best known** of all big dinosaurs, because so many almost-complete fossil skeletons have been found.

- **Famous American fossil hunter** Edward Drinker Cope gave *Camarasaurus* its name in 1877.

- **The name means** 'chambered reptile', because its backbones, or vertebrae, had large, scoop-shaped spaces in them, making them lighter.

- *Camarasaurus* **was up to 21 m long** and had a very bulky, powerful body and legs.

🦶 **North America was home** to *Camarasaurus*, with similar fossils from Europe and Africa given different names.

🦶 **A large, short-snouted head**, similar to that of *Brachiosaurus*, characterized *Camarasaurus*.

🦶 **A fossil skeleton** of a young *Camarasaurus* was uncovered in the 1920s, and had nearly every bone in its body lying in the correct position, as they were when the dinosaur was alive – an amazingly rare find.

◄ *Compared to other sauropods, Camarasaurus had a short neck and tail.*

DID YOU KNOW?

Detailed fossil studies show that one *Camarasaurus* replaced its teeth every 8–9 weeks, and another reached adulthood at 20 years of age and died aged 26.

Diplodocus

- **A huge plant-eating sauropod**, *Diplodocus* lived during the Late Jurassic Period, about 155–145 mya.

- **The first discovery** of *Diplodocus* fossils was in 1877, near Canyon City, Colorado, USA.

- **The main fossils** were found in the USA, in Colorado, Utah and Wyoming.

- **At an incredible 27 m** or more in length, *Diplodocus* is one of the longest dinosaurs known. Some species may have reached 33 m.

- *Diplodocus* **probably** swung its tiny head on its enormous neck to reach fronds and foliage in the trees.

- **Its teeth were slim rods** that formed a comb-like fringe around the front of its mouth.

- *Diplodocus* **may have used** its teeth to strip leaves from twigs and swallow them without chewing.

- **Its nostrils** were once thought to be positioned almost above its eyes. Recent evidence shows they were probably lower down, halfway between the eyes and snout tip.

▼ Diplodocus *was long but light for a sauropod, weighing about 10–25 tonnes.*

Mamenchisaurus

- **A massive plant-eating dinosaur**, *Mamenchisaurus* was similar in appearance to *Diplodocus*.

- **It lived during** the late Jurassic Period, from 160–145 mya.

- **This huge dinosaur** measured about 30 m from nose to tail. Its weight has been estimated at 20–35 tonnes.

- **At up to 15 m**, *Mamenchisaurus* had one of the longest necks of any dinosaur. The neck had up to 19 vertebrae, or neckbones – more than almost any other dinosaur.

- **The remains of *Mamenchisaurus*** were found in China and the dinosaur is named after the place where its fossils were discovered – Mamen Stream.

Other sauropod dinosaurs found in the same region include *Euhelopus* and *Omeisaurus*.

 Mamenchisaurus **may have stretched** out its neck to crop leaves, or – less likely – may have lived in swamps and eaten water plants.

▼ *The joints between the fossil bones of* Mamenchisaurus' *neck show that it was not very flexible.*

DID YOU KNOW?

The species Mamenchisaurus constructus was first named in 1954. Since then another five or six possible species have been identified – although some experts say the remains represent only two or three species.

Scelidosaurus

- **Scelidosaurus was** a medium-sized armoured dinosaur, perhaps an early member of the ankylosaur or stegosaur group.

- **Very well-preserved fossils of *Scelidosaurus*** have been found in Dorset, in southern England. It lived during the Early Jurassic Period, about 190 mya.

- **From nose to tail**, *Scelidosaurus* was about 4 m long.

- **Scelidosaurus probably moved** about on four legs, although it could perhaps rear up to gather food.

- **A plant-eater**, *Scelidosaurus* snipped off its food with the beak-like front of its mouth, and chewed it with its simple, leaf-shaped teeth.

- **Scelidosaurus is one of the earliest** dinosaurs known to have had a set of protective, bony armour plates.

- **A row of bony plates**, or scutes, stuck up from *Scelidosaurus'* neck, back and tail. It also had rows of conical bony plates along its flanks, resembling limpets on a rock.

- **Scelidosaurus was described** and named in 1859 and 1861 by Richard Owen, who also invented the name 'dinosaur'.

▼ Scelidosaurus *was a forerunner of bigger, more heavily armoured dinosaur types, with bony plates called scutes.*

Stegosaurs

- **Plant-eating dinosaurs** that mostly lived around 160–140 mya, stegosaurs are named after the best known of their group, *Stegosaurus*.

- **They are often called** 'plated dinosaurs', from the large, flat plates or slabs of bone on their backs.

- **Stegosaurs probably** first appeared in eastern Asia, then spread to other continents, especially North America and Africa.

- ***Kentrosaurus* was** a 5-m-long stegosaur and weighed an estimated one tonne. Its name means 'spiky reptile'. It lived about 155–150 mya in East Africa.

DID YOU KNOW?

In 2006, fossils of *Stegosaurus* were identified in Portugal, which is the first evidence that this dinosaur lived in Europe.

Most stegosaurs lacked teeth at the front of the mouth, but had horny beaks, like those of birds, for snipping off leaves. They chewed food with small, ridged cheek teeth.

◄ *The back plates of* Kentrosaurus *were taller and narrower than those of* Stegosaurus.

Stegosaurus

- *Stegosaurus* **was the largest** of the stegosaur group. Its fossils were found mainly in present-day Colorado, Utah and Wyoming, USA.

- **Like most of its group**, *Stegosaurus* lived towards the end of the Jurassic Period, about 155–150 mya.

- *Stegosaurus* **was about 8–9 m long** from nose to tail and probably weighed more than 4 tonnes.

- **Its most striking features** were the large, roughly diamond-shaped, leaf-shaped or triangular bony plates along its back.

- **The name** *Stegosaurus* means 'roof reptile'. This is because it was first thought that its bony plates lay flat on its back, overlapping like the tiles on a roof.

- **It is now thought** that the back plates stood upright in two long rows.

- **The plates may have been** for body temperature control, allowing the dinosaur to warm up quickly if it stood side-on to the sun's rays.

- **The back plates** may have been covered with brightly coloured skin, possibly to intimidate enemies – they were too flimsy to provide much protection.

- **Armed with four large spikes**, *Stegosaurus* probably used its tail for swinging at enemies in self-defence.

DID YOU KNOW?

When Stegosaurus fossils were first unearthed in 1876–77, they were thought to be from a large sea turtle, with the back plates lying flat to form its protective shell.

◄ Stegosaurus'
short front limbs
meant that it ate
low-growing plants.

153

Tuojiangosaurus

- *Tuojiangosaurus* **was part** of the stegosaur group. It lived during the Late Jurassic Period, about 170–155 mya.

- **The first nearly complete** dinosaur skeleton to be found in China was of a *Tuojiangosaurus*, and fossil skeletons are on display in several Chinese museums.

- **The name** *Tuojiangosaurus* means 'Tuo River reptile'.

- *Tuojiangosaurus* **was 7 m long** from nose to tail and probably weighed about 3–4 tonnes.

- **Like other stegosaurs**, *Tuojiangosaurus* had tall plates of bone on its back.

The **back plates** were roughly triangular and probably stood upright in two rows that ran from the neck to the middle of the tail.

Tuojiangosaurus **plucked** low-growing plants with its beak-shaped mouth, and partly chewed them with its ridged cheek teeth.

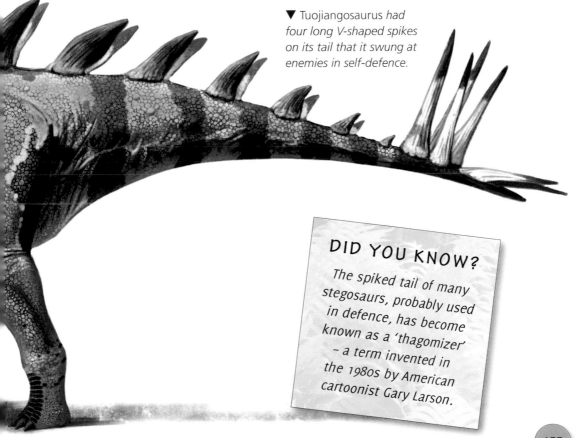

▼ Tuojiangosaurus *had four long V-shaped spikes on its tail that it swung at enemies in self-defence.*

DID YOU KNOW?

The spiked tail of many stegosaurs, probably used in defence, has become known as a 'thagomizer' – a term invented in the 1980s by American cartoonist Gary Larson.

Ankylosaurs

- **Ankylosaurs had** a protective armour of bony plates.

- **Unlike the armoured nodosaurs**, ankylosaurs had a large lump of bone at the end of their tail, which they used as a hammer or club.

- **One of the best known ankylosaurs**, from the preserved remains of about 40 individuals, is *Euoplocephalus*.

- **The hefty *Euoplocephalus*** was about 6 m long and weighed 2 tonnes or more. It lived about 76–75 mya in Alberta, Canada, Montana, USA and other places.

- ***Euoplocephalus* had bony shields** on its head and body, and even had bony eyelids. Blunt spikes ran along its back.

- **Specimens of *Euoplocephalus*** are usually found singly, so it probably didn't live in herds.

- **The ankylosaur *Pinacosaurus*** had bony nodules like chainmail armour in its skin, and rows of blunt spikes from neck to tail.

- **Ankylosaurs had small**, weak teeth, and probably ate soft, low-growing ferns and horsetails.

◀ *The tail club of Euoplocephalus was made from pieces of bone that had fused (stuck) together.*

DID YOU KNOW?
Pinacosaurus was about 5 m long and lived in Asia some 80–75 mya.

Nodosaurs

- **Nodosaurs were a subgroup** of armoured dinosaurs in the main ankylosaur group.

- **The nodosaur subgroup** included *Edmontonia*, *Sauropelta*, *Polacanthus* and *Nodosaurus*.

- **Nodosaurs were slow-moving**, heavy-bodied plant-eaters with thick, heavy nodules, lumps and plates of bone in their skin for protection.

- **Most nodosaurs lived** during the Late Jurassic and Cretaceous Periods, 160–66 mya.

- *Edmontonia* **lived** in North America during the Late Cretaceous Period, 75–66 mya.

- **It was about 7 m long**, but its bony armour made it very heavy for its size, at 4–5 tonnes.

- **Along its neck**, back and tail *Edmontonia* had rows of flat and spiky plates.

- **The nodosaur** *Polacanthus* was about 5 m long and lived 130–120 mya.

Fossils of *Polacanthus* come from the Isle of Wight, England, and perhaps from North America, in South Dakota, USA.

◄ Edmontonia, *one of the last dinosaurs, was covered in many sharp lumps and spikes of bone that gave it some protection from its enemies.*

159

Sauropelta

 Sauropelta was a nodosaur – a type of armoured dinosaur.

 The name *Sauropelta* means 'shielded reptile', from the many large, cone-like lumps of bone – some almost as big as dinner plates – on its head, neck, back and tail.

 The larger lumps of bone on *Sauropelta* were interspersed with smaller, fist-sized bony studs.

DID YOU KNOW?

Sauropelta *lived* 115–110 mya, in present-day Montana and Wyoming, USA.

🐾 *Sauropelta* **was about** 5 m long, including the tail, and probably weighed almost 2 tonnes.

🐾 *Sauropelta* **had a row** of sharp spikes along each side of its body, from just behind the eyes to the tail. The spikes decreased in size towards the tail.

🐾 **The armour** of *Sauropelta* was flexible, almost like lumps of metal set into thick leather, so the dinosaur could twist and turn, but was unable to run fast.

🐾 **Pillar-like legs** supported *Sauropelta's* weight.

🐾 **Using its beak-like mouth**, *Sauropelta* probably plucked its low-growing plant food.

◀ *If attacked, Sauropelta probably crouched down low to protect its soft belly. It may have swung its head to jab at enemies with its long neck spines.*

Estimating size

- **The biggest dinosaurs** were the sauropods such as *Giraffatitan*, *Brachiosaurus* and *Argentinosaurus* – but working out how heavy they were when they were alive is very difficult.

- *Giraffatitan* **is known** from many remains, including almost complete skeletons, so its length is measured accurately – 22 m.

- **A dinosaur's weight** can be estimated from a model of its skeleton, which is 'fleshed out' with clay.

- **The clay represents** muscles, guts and skin, which are based on those of similar reptiles, such as crocodiles, for comparison. Or this is done using a virtual model on a computer. Results give weights of between 20 and 40 tonnes for *Giraffatitan*.

- **The size of the clay model** is estimated by immersing it in water to find its volume.

- **The volume of the model** is scaled up to find the volume of the real dinosaur when it was alive.

- **The sauropod** *Apatosaurus* is now well known from about 12 skeletons, which between them have almost every bone in its body.

- **Experts have 'fleshed out'** the skeleton of *Apatosaurus* by different amounts, so estimates of its weight vary from 15 tonnes to more than 40 tonnes.

- **The length of** *Apatosaurus* is known accurately to have been 21 m in total.

Long neck allowed head to browse widely

▼ *African Giraffatitan had very long front legs, like its North American cousin* Brachiosaurus.

DID YOU KNOW?

The weights and volumes of reptiles alive today are used to calculate the probable weight of a dinosaur when it was alive.

Lesothosaurus and Fabrosaurus

- **There has been much confusion** between two very small plant-eating dinosaurs, *Lesothosaurus* and *Fabrosaurus*.

- **Their fossils come from South Africa** and date back to the Early Jurassic Period, 200–190 mya.

- *Fabrosaurus* **was named** in 1964 from just one fossil specimen of three teeth set in part of a jawbone.

- **Comparing this specimen** with similar fossils from other regions, these indicated a dinosaur plant-eater about one metre long.

- *Lesothosaurus* **received its name** in 1978. Its more plentiful fossils showed a similar one-metre plant-eater to *Fabrosaurus*.

- **Slim and lightly built,** *Lesothosaurus* was only one metre long from nose to tail-tip and would have stood knee-high to an adult human being.

- **Its long, slim back legs** and long toes indicate that *Lesothosaurus* was a fast runner.

- **Teeth and other fossils** of *Lesothosaurus* show that it probably ate low-growing plants such as ferns.

- **The rear teeth were set inwards** slightly from the sides of its skull, suggesting fleshy cheek pouches for storing or chewing food.

- **It is possible that** *Lesothosaurus* and *Fabrosaurus* were the same type of dinosaur. If so, all the fossils should receive the name given first – *Fabrosaurus*.

But the remains of *Fabrosaurus* are so limited, some experts say that it should not even exist as an official name.

 ***Lesothosaurus* may be** a very early type of ornithischian or 'bird-hipped' dinosaur, perhaps on the way to becoming an ornithpod like *Iguanodon* – or a stegosaur or ankylosaur.

▼ Lesothosaurus *may have stood on hind legs to spot danger, much like the mammals called meerkats in the region today.*

Heterodontosaurus

 Heterodontosaurus lived about 200–195 mya, at the beginning of the Jurassic Period.

 A very small dinosaur at only one metre in length (about as long as a large dog), *Heterodontosaurus* would have stood knee-high to a human.

Probably standing partly upright on its longer back legs, *Heterodontosaurus* would have been a fast runner.

Fossils of *Heterodontosaurus* come from Lesotho in southern Africa and Cape Province in South Africa.

Most dinosaurs had teeth of only one shape in their jaws, but *Heterodontosaurus* had three types of teeth.

The front teeth were small, sharp and found only in the upper jaw. They bit against the horny, beak-like lower front of the mouth.

▶ *Small and slim,* Heterodontosaurus *looked similar to meat-eaters such as* Compsognathus, *although it was probably an omnivore (eating anything, plant or animal matter).*

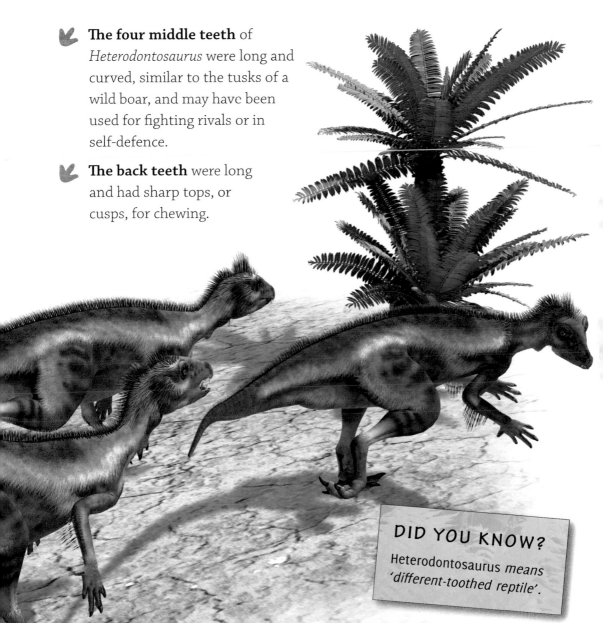

The four middle teeth of *Heterodontosaurus* were long and curved, similar to the tusks of a wild boar, and may have been used for fighting rivals or in self-defence.

The back teeth were long and had sharp tops, or cusps, for chewing.

DID YOU KNOW?

Heterodontosaurus *means 'different-toothed reptile'.*

Iguanodon

- **Part of the ornithopod group**, *Iguanodon* was a large plant-eating dinosaur. It lived during the Early to Middle Cretaceous Period, 130–125 mya.

- **Numerous fossils** of *Iguanodon* have been found in several countries in Europe, especially Belgium, with similar fossils from England, Germany and Spain.

- *Iguanodon* **measured** about 10–11 m from nose to tail. It probably weighed the same as a large elephant – 4–5 tonnes.

- *Iguanodon* **probably walked** and ran on its large, powerful back legs for much of the time, with its body held horizontal.

- **A cone-shaped spike** on the thumb may have been used as a weapon for jabbing at rivals or enemies.

- **The three central fingers** on the hands had hoof-like claws for occasional four-legged walking.

- **The fifth, or little finger**, was able to bend across the hand for grasping objects, and was perhaps used to pull plants towards the mouth.

DID YOU KNOW?
Iguanodon was one of the very first dinosaurs to be given an official scientific name in 1825.

▶ *The thumb spike was used in defence and the fingers grasped food.*

Thumb spike

▼ Iguanodon *is well known from the fossils of many individuals.*

Duckbills

The common name for the hadrosaur group of dinosaurs is 'duckbills'.

Hadrosaurs were big plant-eaters that walked mainly on their two large, powerful rear legs. They were one of the last main dinosaur groups to appear on Earth, less than 100 mya.

Hadrosaurs were named after *Hadrosaurus*, the first dinosaur of the group to be discovered as fossils, found in 1858 in New Jersey, USA.

Most hadrosaurs had wide mouths that were flattened and toothless at the front, like a duck's beak.

Large numbers of cheek teeth filled the back of the hadrosaur's mouth, arranged in rows called batteries. They were ideal for chewing tough plant food.

Some hadrosaurs had tall, elaborate crests or projections of bone on their heads, notably *Corythosaurus*, *Saurolophus* and *Parasaurolophus*.

Hadrosaurs that lacked bony crests and had low, smooth heads included *Anatosaurus*, *Bactrosaurus*, *Kritosaurus* and *Edmontosaurus*.

The name *Hadrosaurus* means 'big reptile'.

Long, relatively narrow tail with a muscular base to swish tail from side to side

DID YOU KNOW?

Edmontosaurus *may have had a loose bag of skin on its nose that it blew up like a balloon to make a honking or trumpeting noise* – perhaps a breeding call.

▼ *Hadrosaurs such as* Corythosarus *are often shown feeding on water plants with their wide, duck-like beaked mouths.*

Possible inflatable bag of skin on snout and forehead

Tall, hollow head crest probably amplified sounds

Wide, beak-like front to mouth

Powerful rear legs for rapid walking and trotting

171

Psittacosaurus

 Psittacosaurus was a plant-eater, and an early relative of the group known as ceratopsians, or 'horn-faced' dinosaurs.

 Appearing in the Middle Cretaceous Period, different species of *Psittacosaurus* lived from 125 to 100 mya.

▼ *In one fossil discovery, an adult* Psittacosaurus *was found with more than 30 young, which it may have been looking after.*

***Psittacosaurus* was named** in 1923 from fossils found in Mongolia, Central Asia. Fossils have been found at various sites across Asia, including Russia, China and Thailand.

 The rear legs of *Psittacosaurus* were longer and stronger than its front legs, suggesting that this dinosaur may have reared up to run fast on its rear legs, rather than running on all four legs.

***Psittacosaurus* measured** about 2 m long, weighed around 20 kg and had four toes on each foot.

The name *Psittacosaurus* means 'parrot reptile', after the dinosaur's beak-shaped mouth, like that of a parrot.

Inside its cheeks, *Psittacosaurus* had many sharp teeth capable of cutting and slicing through tough plant material.

DID YOU KNOW?

Fossil evidence shows that when newly hatched from their eggs, baby Psittacosaurus were hardly longer than a human hand.

Ceratopsians

- **Ceratopsians were large plant-eaters** that appeared less than 120 mya.

- **Ceratopsian fossils** come from Europe, North America and Asia.

- **Ceratopsian means 'horn-face'**, after the long horns on the dinosaurs' snouts, eyebrows or foreheads.

- **Most ceratopsians** had a neck shield or frill that swept sideways and up from the back of the head to cover the upper neck and shoulders.

- **Well known ceratopsians** include *Triceratops*, *Styracosaurus*, *Centrosaurus*, *Pentaceratops*, *Anchiceratops*, *Chasmosaurus* and *Torosaurus*.

- **The neck frills** of some ceratopsians, such as that of *Chasmosaurus*, had large gaps or 'windows' in the bone.

- **The windows in the neck frill** were covered in thick, scaly skin.

- **Ceratopsians had no teeth** in the fronts of their hooked, beak-like mouths.

- **Using rows** of powerful cheek teeth, ceratopsians sheared off their plant food.

DID YOU KNOW?

Torosaurus had one of the longest skulls of any land animal, at about 2.6 m from the front of the snout to the rear of the neck frill.

Chasmosaurus

Styracosaurus

Triceratops

◄ Different ceratopsians had different-shaped frills, horns and spikes.

175

Triceratops

Many fossil remains of *Triceratops* have been found. It is one of the most-studied and best known dinosaurs, and lived at the very end of the Age of Dinosaurs, 68–66 mya.

Triceratops **was the largest** of the plant-eating ceratopsians, or 'horn-faced' dinosaurs.

Fossils of more than 100 *Triceratops* have been discovered in North America, though no truly complete skeletons.

Triceratops **was about 9 m** long and weighed up to 10 tonnes – as big as the largest elephants of today.

As well as a short nose horn and two one-metre eyebrow horns, *Triceratops* also had a wide, sweeping frill that covered its neck like a curved plate.

The neck frill may have been an anchor for the dinosaur's powerful chewing muscles.

Acting as a shield, the bony neck frill may have protected *Triceratops* as it faced predators head-on.

The neck frill may also have been brightly coloured to impress rivals or enemies – or even potential mates.

The beak-like front of *Triceratops*' mouth was toothless, but it had sharp teeth for chewing in its cheeks.

▲ *The beak, head and neck frill of* Triceratops *made up almost a quarter of its length.*

Pachycephalosaurs

 Pachycephalosaurs were one of the last dinosaur groups to appear. Most lived 80–66 mya.

 They are named after one of the best known members of the group, *Pachycephalosaurus*.

 Pachycephalosaurus **means 'thick-headed reptile'**, due to the domed and hugely thickened bone on the top of its skull – like a cyclist's crash helmet.

DID YOU KNOW?

Pachycephalosaurs are often known as the 'bone-heads', 'dome-heads', or 'helmet-heads'.

▶ *Typical of its group,* Pachycephalosaurus *had a thickened layer of bone on the top of its head.*

Extra thick
skull bone

▲ Wannanosaurus *was one of the smallest
pachycephalosaurs, at just one metre long.
Some scientists suggest it had head-butting
contests with rivals, but others say the head
dome was used mainly for defence.*

About 4.5 m long from nose to tail, *Pachycephalosaurus* lived in
the American Midwest.

Stegoceras, also from the American Midwest, was about 2 m long
with a body the size of a goat.

Homalocephale, **about 2 m long**, lived in Asia 80 mya. It had a
flatter skull, but some experts think it was a young *Prenocephale*.

Pachycephalosaurs may have defended themselves by lowering
their heads and charging at their enemies.

At breeding time, the males may have tried to butt each other,
but how and where is not clear.

179

Skin

- **Several fossils of dinosaur skin** have been found, revealing that dinosaurs had scales like today's reptiles.

- **As in crocodiles**, dinosaur scales were embedded in the thick, tough hide, rather than lying on top of the skin and overlapping, as in snakes.

- **When the first fossils** of dinosaur skin were found in the mid-1800s, scientists thought they were from giant prehistoric crocodiles.

- **Fossil skin** of the horned dinosaur *Chasmosaurus* reveals that larger bumps or lumps, called tubercles, were scattered among the normal-sized scales.

▼ Scelidosaurus *was covered from head to tail with hard scutes (bony plates in the skin) and nodules. These would have helped to protect it from meat-eating dinosaurs.*

▲ *Fossil skin, such as this from a hadrosaur, is a relatively rare find.*

🐾 **Fossil skin** of the duckbilled hadrosaur *Edmontosaurus* has also been found.

🐾 *Edmontosaurus* **was covered** in thousands of small scales, like little pebbles, with larger lumps or tubercles spaced among them.

🐾 **Various specimens** of fossil skin show that the scales of *Iguanodon*-type dinosaurs were larger than those of same-sized, similar duckbill dinosaurs.

🐾 **Scaly skin** protected a dinosaur against the teeth and claws of enemies, accidental scrapes, and the bites of pests such as mosquitoes and fleas.

DID YOU KNOW?

Many dinosaur scales were roughly six-sided, which made them both strong and flexible.

Colours

 No one knows for certain what colours most dinosaurs were.

 Some fossil specimens of dinosaur skin show patterns or shading, but all are stone coloured, as fossils are living things that have turned to stone.

 However recent detailed fossil finds have allowed the study of microscopic details of structures called melanosomes in dinosaur feathers, that give clues to colours.

The feathered dinosaur *Sinosauropteryx* probably had white and reddish ginger feathers.

According to some experts, certain dinosaurs may have been bright yellow, red or blue, and possibly striped or patched, like some of today's lizards and snakes.

Some dinosaurs may have been brightly coloured to frighten off predators or to intimidate rivals at breeding time. Colours may have also attracted potential mates.

Tall 'sails' on the backs of the plant-eater *Ouranosaurus* and the meat-eater *Spinosaurus* may have been for visual display, as well as for temperature control.

The large, bony back plates on stegosaurs may have been used for colourful displays to rivals and mates.

The large neck frills of dinosaurs such as *Triceratops* may have been colourful and used for display.

Some dinosaurs may have been similar in colour to crocodiles – dull greens and browns, to help camouflage among trees, rocks and earth.

▲ *The 2-m-long* Dilong *had hair-like feathers, whose tiny structures in well-preserved specimens give some clues to colours. However for the vast majority of reconstructions from fossils, the colours are intelligent guesswork.*

183

Armour

 Many kinds of dinosaurs had protective 'armour'.

 Some armour took the form of bony plates, or osteoderms, embedded in the skin.

 A dinosaur with armour might weigh twice as much as a same-sized dinosaur without armour.

 Armoured dinosaurs are divided into two main groups – the ankylosaurs and the nodosaurs.

▼ *The bony lumps of* Saltasaurus *were scattered over its back and sides.*

 The large sauropod *Saltasaurus*, unusual for its group, had a kind of armour in the form of hundreds of small, bony lumps packed together in the skin of its back.

 On its back, *Saltasaurus* also had about 50 larger pieces of bone, each one the size of a human hand.

- **Saltasaurus is named** after the Salta region of Argentina, where its fossils were found. Its fossils have also been found in Uruguay, South America.

- **Saltasaurus was 12 m long** and weighed about 6–8 tonnes.

Horns

 A dinosaur's horns got bigger as the animal grew. Each horn had a bony core and an outer covering of a tough material formed mainly from keratin – the same substance that makes up human hair and fingernails.

Horns were most common among plant-eating dinosaurs. They were probably used for defence and to protect young against predators.

The biggest horns belonged to the ceratopsians or 'horn-faces', such as *Triceratops*.

In some ceratopsian horns, the bony core alone was about one metre long. This did not include the outer sheath, so the whole horn would have been longer.

**The ceratopsian *Styracosaurus*, or 'spiked reptile', had a series of long horns around the top of its neck frill, and a very long horn on its nose.

Horns may have been used in head-swinging displays to intimidate rivals and make physical fighting less likely.

DID YOU KNOW?

Dinosaurs may have used their horns to push over plants or dig up roots for food.

- **In battle**, male dinosaurs may have locked horns in a trial of strength, as antelopes do today.

- **Armoured dinosaurs** such as the nodosaur *Panoplosaurus* had horn-like spikes along the sides of the body, especially in the shoulder region.

◀ *If an enemy came near, Styracosaurus may have charged with its head down, and jabbed with its long, sharp horn. The wide frill of bone over its neck made it look even more scary.*

187

Head crests

- **Many dinosaurs had lumps**, plates, ridges or other shapes of bone on their heads, called head crests.

- **Head crests** may have been covered with brightly coloured skin for visual display.

- **Meat-eaters with head crests** included *Carnotaurus* and *Dilophosaurus*.

- **The dinosaurs with the largest** and most complicated head crests were the hadrosaurs.

- **The largest head crest** was probably a long, hollow, tubular shape of bone belonging to the hadrosaur *Parasaurolophus*.

- **The head crests of hadrosaurs** may have been involved in making sounds.

- **Some years ago**, the hadrosaur *Tsintaosaurus* was thought to have a very unusual head crest – a hollow tube sticking straight up between the eyes, like a unicorn's horn.

- **The so-called head crest** of *Tsintaosaurus* was then thought to be from another hadrosaur, *Tanius*.

DID YOU KNOW?

The head crests of some large Parasaurolophus, perhaps full-grown males, reached an incredible 1.8 m in length.

🐾 **Then another *Tsintaosaurus* specimen** was found with a similar crest, but more paddle-shaped, so this dinosaur is again regarded as being crested.

▼ *The long crest of* Parasaurolophus *may have had a flap of skin behind it, attached to the lower back of the head.*

189

Teeth

 Some of the most common fossil remains are of dinosaur teeth – the hardest parts of their bodies.

 Dinosaur teeth come in a huge range of sizes and shapes – daggers, knives, shears, pegs, combs, rakes, file-like rasps, crushing batteries and vices.

In some dinosaurs, up to three-quarters of a tooth was fixed into the jaw bone, so only one-quarter showed.

The teeth of plant-eaters such as *Iguanodon* had angled tops that rubbed past each other in a grinding motion.

▼ Tyrannosaurus *had 50-plus 'banana' teeth. They were long and strong for tearing flesh and crushing bone.*

- **Some duckbill dinosaurs** (hadrosaurs) had more than 1000 teeth, all at the back of the mouth.

- **Like modern reptiles**, dinosaurs probably grew new teeth to replace old, worn or broken ones.

- **Some of the largest teeth** of any dinosaur belonged to 9-m-long *Daspletosaurus*, a tyrannosaur-like meat-eater. They measured up to 18 cm in length.

▼ Edmontosaurus *had no front teeth, only a flattened 'duck-bill'.*

Edmontosaurus had batteries of teeth for crushing plants

Beaks

 Several kinds of dinosaurs had a toothless, beak-shaped front to their mouths.

 Beaked dinosaurs included ceratopsians (horn-faces) such as *Triceratops*, ornithopods such as *Iguanodon* and the hadrosaurs (duckbills), stegosaurs, ankylosaurs (armoured dinosaurs) and fast-running ostrich dinosaurs.

▶ Hadrosaurs, or duckbill dinosaurs, such as this *Lambeosaurus*, had a wide, flat front to the mouth, like a duck's beak. These large plant eaters probably used their sharp beaks to slice through plant food, which was chewed by batteries of flat teeth that were constantly being replaced.

▶ Protoceratops *had a tall skull with deep jaws tipped by a sharp beak.*

🐾 **Most beaked dinosaurs** had chopping or chewing teeth near the backs of their mouths, in their cheeks, but ostrich dinosaurs had no teeth.

🐾 **A dinosaur's beak** was made up of the upper (maxilla) and the lower (dentary or mandible) jaw bones.

🐾 **The bones at the front** of a dinosaur's jaw would have been covered with horn, which formed the outer shape of the beak.

🐾 **Dinosaurs almost certainly used** their beaks for pecking, snipping, tearing and slicing their food. They may also have used their beaks to peck fiercely at any attackers.

DID YOU KNOW?

Some of the largest beaks in relation to body size belonged to Oviraptor and Psittacosaurus.

193

Noses

- **Dinosaurs breathed** through their mouths and/or noses, like many other creatures today.

- **Fossil dinosaur skulls** show that there were two nose openings, called nares, in the bone.

- **The nasal openings**, or nares, led to nasal chambers inside the skull, where the smell organs were located.

- **Some meat-eaters**, especially carnosaurs such as *Allosaurus* and *Tyrannosaurus*, had very large nasal chambers and probably had an excellent sense of smell.

- **In most dinosaurs**, the nasal openings were at the front of the snout, just above the upper jaw.

- **In some dinosaurs**, especially sauropods such as *Mamenchisaurus* and *Brachiosaurus*, the nasal openings were higher on the skull, between the eyes.

- **Fossils show** that air passages led backwards from the nasal chambers into the head for breathing.

DID YOU KNOW?

In hadrosaurs, the nasal passages inside the bony head crests were more than one metre long.

🦖 **The nasal openings** led to external openings, or nostrils, in the skin.

🦖 **New evidence from modern animals** suggests that a dinosaur's nostrils would have been lower down than the nares, towards the front of the snout.

▼ *The nares (nasal openings) at the snout tip of* Tyrannosaurus *were especially large.*

Nares

195

Eyes

No fossils have been found of dinosaur eyes because they were made of soft tissue that soon rotted away after death, or they were eaten by scavengers.

▼ Tyrannosaurus rex *had large eyes that were set at an angle so they looked more to the front rather than to the sides. This allowed* T rex *to see an object in front with both eyes and so judge its distance well.*

▶ *The eye socket of* Troodon *was very large, shown here as the elongated middle opening.*

The main clues to dinosaur eyes come from the bowl-like hollows, or orbits, in the skull where the eyes were located.

The orbits in fossil skulls show that dinosaur eyes were similar to those of reptiles today.

The 6-m-long sauropod *Vulcanodon* had tiny eyes relative to the size of its head.

Small-eyed dinosaurs probably only had good vision in the daytime.

The eyes of many plant-eating dinosaurs, such as *Vulcanodon*, were on the sides of their heads, giving them all-round vision.

The small meat-eater *Troodon* had relatively large eyes, and it could probably see well, even in dim light.

Troodon's **eyes** were on the front of its face and pointed forwards, allowing it to see detail and judge distance.

Dinosaurs that had large bulges, called optic lobes, in their brains – detectable by the shapes of their skulls – could probably see very well, perhaps even at night.

DID YOU KNOW?

The plant-eater Leaellynasaura had large optic lobes, and probably had good eyesight.

197

Brains

- **There is a broad link** between the size of an animal's brain compared to the size of its body, and the level of intelligence it shows.

- **Some fossil dinosaur skulls** have preserved the hollow where the brain once was, revealing its approximate size and shape.

- **In some cases**, a lump of rock formed inside a fossil skull, taking on the size and shape of the brain.

- **The tiny brain** of *Stegosaurus* weighed about 70–80 g, while the whole dinosaur weighed perhaps 4 tonnes.

- **The brain** of *Stegosaurus* was only 1/50,000th of the weight of its whole body (in a human it is 1/50th).

- ***Brachiosaurus'* brain** was perhaps only 1/100,000th of the weight of its whole body.

- **The brain of the small meat-eater** *Troodon* was about 1/100th the weight of its body, which means that *Troodon* was probably one of the most intelligent dinosaurs.

- **The brain-body size comparison** for most dinosaurs is much the same as that of living reptiles.

- **Small- and medium-sized** meat-eaters such as *Troodon* may have been as 'intelligent' as parrots or rats.

- **It was once thought** that *Stegosaurus* had a 'second brain' in the base of its tail. Now this lump is thought to have been a nerve junction.

▶ Camarasaurus *had one of the smallest brains for its body size of any dinosaur – about the size of a human fist.*

▲ *Small meat-eaters such as* Troodon *had the biggest brains for their body size, and probably showed the most intelligence.*

199

Stomach stones

- **Some dinosaur fossils** are found with smooth, rounded stones, like seashore pebbles, jumbled up among or near them.

- **Smooth pebbles occur** with dinosaur fossils far more than would be expected by chance alone.

- **These stones** are mainly found with or near the remains of large plant-eating dinosaurs, especially prosauropods such as *Massospondylus*, *Plateosaurus* and *Riojasaurus*, sauropods such as *Brachiosaurus* and *Diplodocus*, the parrot-beaked *Psittacosaurus* and the stegosaurs.

- **Some plant-eating dinosaurs** may have used smooth stones to help process their food.

- **The smooth pebbles** associated with dinosaur remains are known as gastroliths.

- **Gastroliths were stones** that a dinosaur deliberately swallowed.

◄ *Gastroliths as small as a pea and as large as a football have been found.*

🦶 **In the stomach**, gastroliths acted as 'millstones', crushing and churning food, and breaking it down into a soft pulp for better digestion.

🦶 **As gastroliths churned** and rubbed inside a dinosaur's guts, they became very rounded, smoothed and polished.

🦶 **Gastroliths may be the reason** why many big plant-eaters, especially sauropods, had no chewing teeth – the mashing was done inside the guts.

▼ *Sauropods, like Barosaurus, swallowed stones that ground up their food in a part of the digestive system called the gizzard. This meant that no feeding time was wasted in chewing.*

KEY
1 Gullet
2 Crop
3 Windpipe
4 Heart
5 Liver
6 Lung
7 Gizzard (stomach)
8 Small intestine
9 Large intestine
10 Kidney

201

Sails

- **Long, bony extensions**, like rods or spines, stuck up from the backs of some dinosaurs.

- **These extensions** may have held up a large area of skin, commonly called a back sail.

- **Dinosaurs with back sails** included the meat-eater *Spinosaurus* and the plant-eater *Ouranosaurus*.

- *Spinosaurus* and *Ouranosaurus* both lived over 100 mya.

- **Fossils of *Spinosaurus*** and *Ouranosaurus* were found in North Africa.

- **The skin on a back sail** may have been brightly coloured, or may even have changed colour, like the skin of a chameleon lizard today.

- **Colours and patterns** could be used to startle enemies, deter rivals, and impress mates at breeding time.

- **A back sail** may have helped to control body temperature. Standing sideways to the sun, it would absorb the sun's heat and allow the dinosaur to warm up quickly.

- **Standing in the shade**, a back sail would lose warmth and help the dinosaur to avoid overheating.

▶ *Apart from its back sail,* Ouranosaurus *was similar to its close cousin, the plant-eater* Iguanodon.

Hips

- **All dinosaurs are classified** in one of two large groups, according to the design and shape of their hip bones.

- **One of these groups** is the Saurischia, meaning 'reptile-hipped'.

- **In a saurischian dinosaur**, the pubis bones (the lower front pair of rod-shaped bones in the pelvis) project down and forwards.

- **Almost all meat-eating dinosaurs** belonged to the Saurischia.

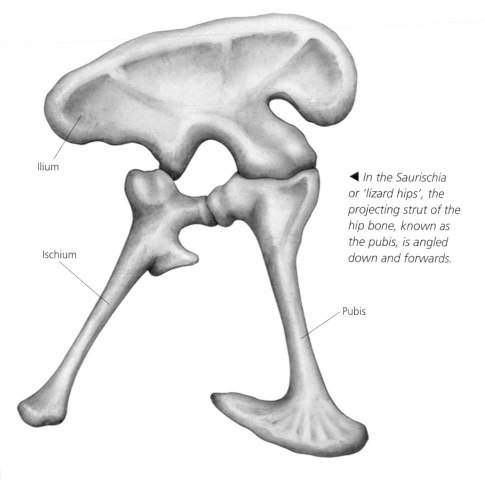

Ilium

Ischium

Pubis

◄ *In the Saurischia or 'lizard hips', the projecting strut of the hip bone, known as the pubis, is angled down and forwards.*

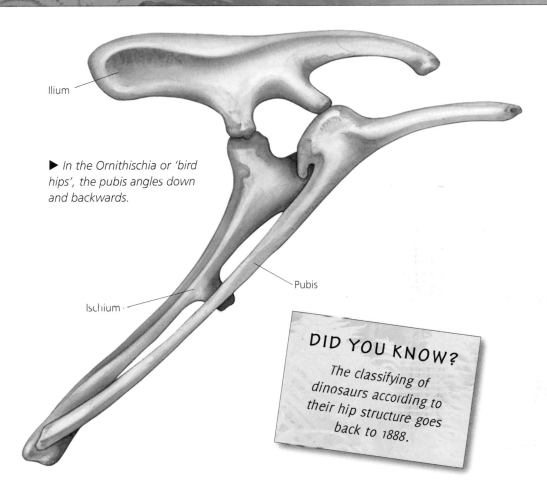

Ilium

▶ *In the Ornithischia or 'bird hips', the pubis angles down and backwards.*

Pubis

Ischium

DID YOU KNOW?

The classifying of dinosaurs according to their hip structure goes back to 1888.

🐾 **The biggest dinosaurs**, the plant-eating sauropods, also belonged to the Saurischia.

🐾 **The second group** is the Ornithischia, meaning 'bird-hipped'.

🐾 **In an ornithischian dinosaur**, the pubis bones project down and backwards, lying parallel with another pair, the ischium bones.

🐾 **All dinosaurs** in the Ornithischia group, from small *Heterodontosaurus* to huge *Triceratops*, were plant-eaters.

205

Legs and posture

All dinosaurs had four limbs. Unlike some other reptiles, such as snakes and slow-worms, they did not lose their limbs through evolution.

Some dinosaurs, such as the massive, plant-eating sauropod *Janenschia*, stood and walked on all four legs nearly all the time.

The all-fours method of standing and walking is called 'quadrupedal'.

Some dinosaurs, such as the nimble, meat-eating dromaeosaur *Deinonychus*, stood and walked on their back limbs only.

The back-limbs-only method of standing and walking is called bipedal.

Some dinosaurs, such as the hadrosaur *Edmontosaurus*, could move on all four limbs or just on their back legs if they chose to.

◄ Brachiosaurus *had the typical quadrupedal posture, using all four legs.*

▲ Tarbosaurus, *an Asian type of* Tyrannosaurus, *was a bipedal dinosaur that ran and walked on its back legs. Its strong rear legs contrasted hugely to its puny front arms, which were too small to be used.*

- **The two- or four-legs method** of standing and walking is called 'bipedal/quadrupedal'.

- **Reptiles such as lizards** and crocodiles have a sprawling posture, in which the upper legs join the body at the sides.

- **Dinosaurs had an upright posture**, with the legs directly below the body.

- **The more efficient upright posture** and gait may be one major reason why dinosaurs were so successful compared to other animals of the time.

Feet

- **Dinosaur feet differed**, depending on the animal's body design, weight and lifestyle.

- **A typical dinosaur's front feet** had metacarpal bones in the lower wrist or upper hand, and two or three phalanges bones in each digit (finger or toe), tipped by claws.

- **The rear feet** of a typical dinosaur had metatarsal (instead of metacarpal) bones in the lower ankle.

- **Some dinosaurs** had five toes per foot, like most other reptiles (and most birds and mammals).

- **Sauropods probably had feet** with rounded bases supported by a wedge of fibrous, cushion-like tissue.

▲ *A* Tyrannosaurus *had three clawed toes per foot.*

- **Most sauropods had claws** on their first two or three toes, and smaller, blunter 'hooves' on the other two toes.

- **Ostrich dinosaurs** such as *Gallimimus* had very long feet and long, slim toes for running fast.

- **Many fast-running dinosaurs** had fewer toes, to reduce weight – *Gallimimus* had three toes per back foot.

The ornithopod, or 'bird feet' dinosaur group, includes *Iguanodon*, duckbilled dinosaurs, *Heterodontosaurus* and many other plant-eaters.

DID YOU KNOW?

The dinosaur group that includes all the meat-eaters, both large and small, is named the theropods, or 'beast feet'.

▶ The living ostrich has two toes per foot, the inner one – the first or big toe – being larger and claw-tipped.

209

Claws

- **Like reptiles today**, dinosaurs had claws or similar hard structures at the ends of their digits (fingers and toes).

- **Dinosaur claws** were probably made from keratin – the same hard substance that formed their horns, and from which our own fingernails and toenails are made.

- **Claw shapes and sizes** relative to body size varied greatly between dinosaurs.

- **In many meat-eating dinosaurs** that ran on two back legs, the claws on the fingers were long and sharp, similar to a cat's claws.

- **A small, meat-eating dinosaur** such as *Troodon* probably used its finger claws for grabbing small mammals and lizards, and for scrabbling in the soil for insects and worms.

- **Larger meat-eating dinosaurs** such as *Allosaurus* may have used their hand claws to hold and slash their prey.

- **Huge plant-eating sauropods** such as *Diplodocus* had claws on its elephant-like feet that resembled nails or hooves.

- **Many dinosaurs** had five-clawed digits on their feet, but some, such as *Tyrannosaurus*, had only three.

- **The largest animal claws** belonged to the 'scythe lizards' or therizinosaur dinosaurs – some were more than one metre long.

▲ *The fingers and claws of* Deinonychus *were especially long and strong.*

Deinonychus **had long claws** on its hands and feet that it used to slash at prey. Its name means 'terrible claw' and it lived in the Mid-Cretaceous Period.

211

Tails

 All dinosaurs evolved with tails – though some individuals may have lost theirs in attacks or accidents.

 The length of the tail relative to the body, and its shape, thickness and special features, gives many clues as to how the dinosaur used it.

The longest tails, at more than 17 m, belonged to the giant plant-eating sauropods such as *Diplodocus*.

Some sauropods had a chain of more than 80 separate caudal vertebrae (bones in the tail) – more than twice the usual number.

▼ Compsognathus *had a long tail that helped it to balance and turn quickly when it was running fast.*

► The 10-m sauropod Shunosaurus *lived in China 170 mya. It had a tail club with added spikes, which would have made a powerful weapon for self-defence.*

Sauropods may have used their tails as a whip to flick at enemies.

Many meat-eating dinosaurs that stood or ran on their back legs had thick-based tails to balance the weight of their bodies.

Small meat-eaters, such as *Compsognathus*, used their tails for balance when leaping and darting about.

The meat-eater *Ornitholestes* had a tail that was more than half of its 2-m length. It was used as a counterbalance and rudder to help it turn corners at speed.

Armoured dinosaurs called ankylosaurs had two huge lumps of bone at the ends of their tails, which they swung at their enemies like a club.

The tails of duckbilled dinosaurs (hadrosaurs) may have been swished from side to side in the water as an aid to swimming.

213

Male and female

 In dinosaur fossils, the shapes of the hip bones and head crests can indicate if the creatures were male or female.

Head crest fossils of different sizes and proportions belonging to the hadrosaur (duckbilled dinosaur) *Lambeosaurus* have been found.

Some *Lambeosaurus* had short, rounded main crests with small, spike-like spurs pointing up and back.

- **Other *Lambeosaurus*** had a large, angular main crest with a large spur pointing up and back.

- **The head crest differences** in *Lambeosaurus* fossils may indicate that males and females looked different.

- **Remains of the hadrosaur** *Corythosaurus* show two main sizes of head crest, perhaps one belonging to females and the other to males.

- **New studies** in the variations of head crests led to about ten different species of these dinosaurs being reclassified as just two species of *Corythosaurus*.

DID YOU KNOW?

In Parasaurolophus specimens, some head crests were twice as long as others – probably a male-female difference.

◀ *Male and female* Lambeosaurus *may have had different-shaped head crests, with this individual being male. The crests may also have become relatively larger compared to body size as the dinosaurs grew.*

215

Warm or cold blood?

- **If dinosaurs were cold-blooded**, like reptiles today, they would have been slow or inactive in cold conditions.

- **If dinosaurs were warm-blooded**, like birds and mammals today, they would have been able to stay warm and active in cold conditions.

- **Experts once believed** that all dinosaurs were cold-blooded, but today there is much disagreement.

▼ *The 'Willo' specimen in 1993 was identified as the fossilized heart of a small plant-eating dinosaur,* Thescelosaurus, *with similarities to a bird or mammal heart. However it may well be simply a natural rock formation.*

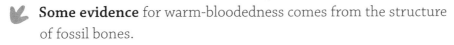

▶ *Crocodiles, which were around even in the very earliest dinosaur period (the Triassic) are cold-blooded.*

Some evidence for warm-bloodedness comes from the structure of fossil bones.

The structure of some dinosaur bones is more like that of warm-blooded creatures than of reptiles.

Some small meat-eating dinosaurs very probably evolved into birds. As birds are warm-blooded, these dinosaurs may have been warm-blooded too.

If some dinosaurs were warm-blooded, they would probably have needed to eat at least ten times more food than if they were cold-blooded, to 'burn' food energy to make heat.

In a 'snapshot' count of dinosaur fossils, the number of predators compared to prey is more like the comparisons seen in mammals than in reptiles.

Many small meat-eaters are now known to have had feathers. One reason could be as insulation, to keep in body heat if the dinosaur was warm-blooded.

217

Speed

- **The fastest dinosaurs** had long, slim, muscular legs and small, lightweight bodies.

- **Ostrich dinosaurs** were probably the speediest, perhaps attaining the same top speed as today's ostrich – 70 km/h.

- **The main leg muscles** of the ostrich dinosaur *Struthiomimus* were in its hips and thighs.

- **The hip and leg design** of ostrich dinosaurs meant they could swing their limbs to and fro quickly, like those of a modern racehorse.

- **Large, powerful, plant-eating dinosaurs**, such as the duckbill *Edmontosaurus*, may have pounded along on their huge back legs at 40 km/h.

- **Plant-eaters** such as *Iguanodon* and *Muttaburrasaurus* may have trotted along at 10–12 km/h for many hours.

- **Some experts** once suggested that the great meat-eater *Tyrannosaurus* may have been able to run at 50 km/h.

- **Other experts think** *Tyrannosaurus* was a relatively slow runner at 20 km/h.

- **The slowest dinosaurs** were giant sauropods such as *Brachiosaurus*, which probably plodded at 4–6 km/h (about human walking speed).

- **The fastest land animal today**, the cheetah, would beat any dinosaur with its maximum burst of speed of more than 100 km/h.

▼ In 2007, computer predictions based on data taken from fossils suggested that the top speed of Tyrannosaurus may have been about 28 km/h.

Coprolites

- **Coprolites are the fossilized droppings**, or dung, of animals from long ago, such as dinosaurs. Like other fossils, they have become solid rock.

- **Thousands of dinosaur coprolites** have been found at fossil sites across the world.

- **Cracking or cutting** open coprolites may reveal what the dinosaur had eaten.

- **Coprolites produced** by large meat-eaters such as *Tyrannosaurus* contain bone from their prey.

- **The microscopic structure** of the bones found in coprolites shows the age of the prey when it was eaten. Most victims were very young or old, as these were the easiest creatures for a predator to kill.

- **Coprolites produced** by small meat-eaters such as *Compsognathus* may contain the hard bits of insects, such as the legs and wing cases of beetles.

Huge piles of coprolites found in Montana, USA, were probably produced by the large plant-eater *Maiasaura*.

Maiasaura **coprolites** contain the remains of cones, buds and the needle-like leaves of conifer trees, showing that these dinosaurs had a diet of tough plant matter.

◄ *These coprolites are probably from Titanosaurus. Plant debris can be clearly seen on the surface.*

DID YOU KNOW?

One of the largest dinosaur coprolites found measures 44 cm in length and was probably produced by Tyrannosaurus.

221

Footprints

Fossilized dinosaur footprints have been found all over the world.

Some dinosaurs left footprints when they walked on the soft mud or sand of riverbanks. Then the mud baked hard in the sun, and was covered by more sand or mud, which helped preserve the footprints as fossils.

Some footprints were made when dinosaur feet left impressions in soft mud or sand that was then covered by volcanic ash, which set hard.

Many footprints have been found together in lines, called 'trackways'. These suggest that some dinosaurs lived in groups, or used the same routes regularly.

- **The distance between** same-sized footprints indicates whether a dinosaur was walking, trotting or running.

- **Footprints of big meat-eaters** such as *Tyrannosaurus* show three toes with claws, on a forward-facing foot.

- **In big plant-eaters**, such as *Iguanodon*, each footprint shows three separate toes, but less or no claw impressions, and the feet point slightly inwards.

- **In giant plant-eating sauropods**, each footprint is rounded and has indentations of nail-like 'hooves'.

- **Some sauropod footprints** are more than one metre across.

DID YOU KNOW?

In 2009 sauropod footprints 1.7 m across were found in the Jura region of France.

▲ Fossilized footprints are called trace fossils because they are signs or prints made by dinosaurs, or other creatures, rather than actual body parts.

Herds

- **When fossils of many individuals** of the same dinosaur type are found together, there are various possible causes.

- **One reason is because** their bodies were swept to the same place by a flood, although they may have originally been living in different places.

- **The dinosaurs may have died** in the same place if they had lived there as a group or herd.

- **There is much evidence** that various dinosaur types lived in groups or herds, examples being *Diplodocus*, *Triceratops* and *Iguanodon*.

- **Many fossil footprints** found together heading the same way also suggest that some dinosaurs lived in herds.

- **Some fossil groups** include dinosaurs of different ages, from babies to youngsters and adults.

- **Footprints of a plant-eating dinosaur** have been found with the prints of a meat-eater to one side of them – perhaps evidence of a hunter pursuing its victim.

- **Prints all pointing** in the same direction indicate a herd travelling together to the same place.

- **Sometimes larger footprints** are found to the sides of smaller ones, possibly indicating that adults guarded their young between them.

- **Many jumbled prints** in what was once mud suggests a group of dinosaurs came to drink at a riverbank or lakeside.

▶ *A mixed-age herd would have left similar footprints of different sizes.*

DID YOU KNOW?

At Peace River Canyon, British Columbia, Canada, some 1700 footprints were found.

Migration

- **Today, almost no land reptiles** go on regular, long-distance journeys, called migrations.

- **Over the past 30 years**, some scientists have suggested that certain dinosaurs regularly migrated.

- **Evidence for migrating dinosaurs** comes from the positions of the continents at the time. In certain regions, cool winters would have prevented the growth of enough plants for dinosaurs to eat.

- **Fossil evidence suggests** that some plants stopped growing during very hot or dry times, so some dinosaurs would have migrated to find food.

- **The footprints or tracks** of many dinosaurs travelling in herds is possible evidence that some dinosaurs migrated.

- **Dinosaurs that may have migrated** include *Pachyrhinosaurus*, sauropods such as *Diplodocus* and *Camarasaurus*, and ornithopods such as *Iguanodon* and *Muttaburrasaurus*.

- **One huge fossil site** in Alberta, Canada, contains the fossils of about 1000 *Pachyrhinosaurus* – perhaps a migrating herd that got caught in a flood.

- **In North America**, huge herds of horned dinosaurs may have migrated north for the brief sub-Arctic summer.

- **In 2012, teeth from *Camarasaurus*** suggested they migrated perhaps 300 km each way to avoid the dry season.

▶ *Fossils of* Pachyrhinosaurus *have been found in parts of Alaska that were inside the Arctic Circle at the end of the Cretaceous Period. It is possible they migrated here from farther south.*

DID YOU KNOW?
Migrating Centrosaurus may have walked 100 km a day.

Hibernation

- **Dinosaurs may have** gone into an inactive state called torpor or 'hibernation' during cold periods, as many reptiles do today.

- **The plant-eater** *Leaellynasaura*, found at Dinosaur Cove, Australia, may have become torpid due to the yearly cycle of seasons there.

- **Dinosaur Cove** was nearer the South Pole when dinosaurs lived there, 110–105 mya. At this time, the climate was relatively warm, with no ice at the North or South Poles.

- **Dinosaurs living** at Dinosaur Cove would have had to cope with periods of darkness in winter. They may have become torpid to survive the cold.

- **The eye and brain shapes** of *Leaellynasaura* suggest it had good eyesight, which would have helped it to see in the winter darkness, or in dim forests.

- **Dinosaur fossils** have been found in the Arctic region near the North Pole.

- **Arctic dinosaurs** either became torpid in winter, or migrated south to warmer regions.

▼ Leaellynasaura *may have
slept through the cold season,
perhaps protected in a burrow.
This 3-m dinosaur had a longer
tail, in proportion to size, than
almost any other dinosaur.*

DID YOU KNOW?

Leaellynasaura means
'Leaellyn's lizard/reptile',
named after Leaellyn Rich,
the young daughter of
the palaeontolgists who
discovered its fossils.

Sounds

- **Few reptiles today** make complicated sounds, except for simple hisses, grunts, coughs and roars.

- **Fossils suggest** that dinosaurs made a variety of sounds in several different ways.

- **The bony, hollow head crests** of duckbills (hadrosaurs) may have been used for making sounds.

- **The head crests** of some hadrosaurs contained tubes called respiratory airways, which were used for breathing.

- **Air blown forcefully** through a hadrosaur's head crest passages could have made the whole crest vibrate.

- **A vibrating head crest** may have made a loud sound like a honk, roar or bellow – similar to an elephant trumpeting with its trunk.

- **Fossil skulls** of some hadrosaurs, such as *Edmontosaurus* and *Kritosaurus*, suggest that there was a loose flap of skin, like a floppy bag, between the nostrils and the eyes.

DID YOU KNOW?

By blowing through models of hadrosaur head crests, a wide range of sounds can be made – similar to those of brass and wind instruments!

▶ *Inside the mostly hollow head crest of the hadrosaur* Lambeosaurus, *the airways or nasal passages followed a winding route.*

***Kritosaurus* may have inflated** its loose nasal flap of skin like a balloon to make a honking or bellowing sound, as some seals do today.

Bony outer layer of crest

Winding air passages

Skull bone

Nostril

Outer skin

Nests

 There are hundreds of discoveries of fossil dinosaur eggs and nests, found with the parent dinosaurs.

Eggs and nests of the plant-eater *Protoceratops*, an early kind of horned dinosaur, were found in 2011.

Some of the nests once thought to be of *Protoceratops* are now believed to belong to *Oviraptor*.

Many of these nests were found in a small area, showing that these dinosaurs bred in colonies.

The nests were shallow, bowl-shaped pits about one metre across, scraped in the earth.

The eggs were probably covered with earth and incubated by the heat of the sun.

New nests had been made on top of old ones, showing that the colony was used year after year.

Nests and eggs of the plant-eater *Orodromeus* have been found in Montana, USA.

In each nest, about 20 *Orodromeus* eggs were neatly arranged in a spiral, starting with one in the centre and working outwards.

▼ Various clues from fossil evidence show that the hadrosaur Maiasaura may have brought food back to its newly hatched young in the nest. Whether one parent or both did is not known.

DID YOU KNOW?

Some preserved nests of Maiasaura babies contain traces of fossil buds and leaves – perhaps food brought to them by a parent.

Hatchling

Unhatched egg

233

Eggs

 Fossil finds since the 1970s show that some dinosaurs may have looked after their young.

Fossils of the small parrot-beaked dinosaur *Psittacosaurus* suggest one adult may have guided and guarded many young.

 These fossils were probably preserved when the adult and young sheltered in a cave that collapsed on them all.

Many fossils of adult *Maiasaura* have been found, together with its nests, eggs and hatchlings (newly hatched young).

 Fossils of *Maiasaura* come mainly from Montana, USA and are about 75 million years old. The main fossil area is nicknamed 'Egg Mountain'.

There are remains of more than 100 *Maiasaura* specimens of different ages.

The teeth of *Maiasaura* babies found in the nest are slightly worn, suggesting that they had eaten food.

The leg bones and joints of the *Maiasaura* babies were not quite fully formed, showing that they were not yet able to move about to gather their own food.

Evidence from the *Maiasaura* nesting sites shows the nests were about 7 m apart, which would just allow room for a 9–m adult. Each nest had up to 40 eggs laid in spiral pattern.

The name *Maiasaura* means 'good mother reptile' and was given in 1979 by US palaeontologists John 'Jack' Horner and Robert Makela.

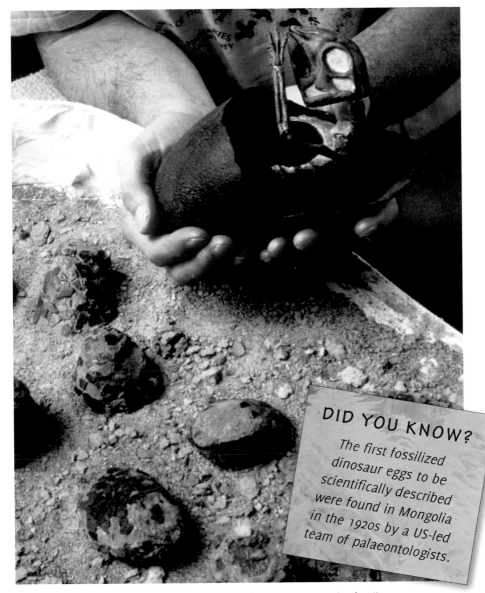

▲ *A cast of a baby* Maiasaura *duckbill dinosaur, among the fossil remains of a nest site. These fossils were discovered in Montana, USA.*

Growth

 In very well-preserved fossils sometimes fine details can be seen as lines, rings and other marks relating to how the dinosaur or other animal grew through the seasons and years.

The spacing of the marks may show slow or limited growth due to food shortage, disease or severe climate conditions. Marks farther apart indicate faster growth, for example, with plentiful food.

More than 60 dinosaur bones have been studied in this way to assess growth speed at different ages.

The bones included *Tyrannosaurus* and its smaller cousins *Albertosaurus*, at up to 2 tonnes, and *Daspletosaurus* at 2–3 tonnes.

Results show all three kinds of dinosaurs grew especially fast in adolescence.

Albertosaurus* and *Daspletosaurus had growth spurts at around 11–15 years of age, when they put on an estimated 0.3–0.5 kg of weight – every day.

◀ *A young* Tyrannosaurus *had slightly different proportions to the adult shown here, with a shorter, rounder snout and slimmer limbs. The great predator was fully grown by the age of about 20 years.*

🦶 ***Tyrannosaurus* gained weight** between 14 and 18 years old. During its peak growth spurt, it put on 2 kg daily.

🦶 **This growth surge meant** that a fully grown adult *Tyrannosaurus* was two to three times heavier than *Albertosaurus* and *Daspletosaurus*.

237

Age and lifespan

- **Detailed studies of the growth lines** and rings in very well-preserved fossils reveal how long dinosaurs and other prehistoric creatures lived.

- **Analysis of *Tyrannosaurus* bones** showed that by 20 years of age, and weighing around 5 tonnes, they almost stopped growing during adulthood.

- **The oldest and biggest specimen** of *Tyrannosaurus*, nicknamed 'Sue', died at 28 years of age.

- **Other estimates of dinosaur growth** rates and ages come from comparisons with today's birds, mammals and reptiles.

- **Some reptiles today** continue to grow throughout their lives, although their growth rate slows with age, while birds reach adult size in one or two years, then do not grow any more.

- **Like many animals today**, a dinosaur's growth rate probably depended largely on its food supply, the temperature, disease and other factors.

- **Small meat-eating dinosaurs** such as *Compsognathus* may have lived to be only five to eight years old.

- **A giant sauropod probably lived** to be 50 years old, or even more than 100 years old.

- **During its lifetime**, a big sauropod such as *Brachiosaurus* would have increased its weight 2000 times (compared to 20 times in a human).

DID YOU KNOW?

The longest-lived land animals today are reptiles – the giant tortoises and other tortoise species. There are several recorded ages of 150–200 years, with a few claims for over 250 years.

▼ Crocodiles frequently exceed 50 years of age, and some may reach 100, while alligators have been recorded at 50–60 years old.

239

Europe

The first dinosaur fossils ever discovered and given official names were found in England in the 1820s.

One of the first almost complete dinosaur skeletons found was that of the big plant-eater *Iguanodon*, in 1871, in southern England.

Some of the most numerous early fossils found were those of *Iguanodon*, discovered in the Belgian village of Bernissart in 1878.

About 155–145 mya, Solnhofen in southern Germany was a mosaic of lush islands and shallow lagoons – ideal for many kinds of life.

At Solnhofen, amazingly detailed fossils of tiny *Compsognathus* and the first-known bird *Archaeopteryx* have been found preserved in sandstone.

Elgin (Scotland)
Ockley (England)
Stonesfield (England)
Halberstadt (Germany)
Kelheim (Germany)
Trossingen (Germany)
Charmouth (England)
Bernissart (Belgium)
Solnhofen (Germany)
Friek (Switzerland)
Swanage (England)
Isle of Wight (England)
Nice (France)
Aix-en-Provence (France)
Torres Vedras (Portugal)
Morella (Spain)

◀ *The dots indicate just a few of the dinosaur fossil sites found in Europe.*

- **Fossils of *Compsognathus*** were also found near Nice in southern France.

- **Many fossils** of *Plateosaurus* were recovered from Trossingen, Germany, in 1911–12, 1921–23 and 1932.

- **Some of the largest fossil eggs**, measuring 30 cm long, were thought to have been laid by *Hypselosaurus* near Aix-en-Provence in southern France.

- **The Isle of Wight** off southern England has provided so many dinosaur fossils that it is sometimes known as 'Dinosaur Island'.

- **Fossils of *Hypsilophodon*** have been found in eastern Spain, and those of *Camptosaurus* on the coast of Portugal.

▲ *One of the first really big dinosaurs was* Plateosaurus, *or 'flat reptile'. Its front feet could be hyper-extended. This flexibility meant that* Plateosaurus *may have been able to grasp branches while feeding.*

▶ *During the Jurassic Period, much of Europe would have looked like this. There was a much more tropical climate where ferns, ginkgoes, horsetails and cycads flourished alongside forests of conifers and tree ferns.*

241

Africa

The first major discoveries of dinosaur fossils in Africa were made in 1907, at Tendaguru, present-day Tanzania. They included *Giraffatitan*, *Dicraeosaurus*, and the stegosaur-like *Kentrosaurus*.

Remains of *Cetiosaurus* were found in Morocco, north Africa.

Nigersaurus, a 9-m, 10-tonne plant-eater, is known from fossils found in Niger. It had huge numbers of teeth, more than 500 at any one time.

Fossils of *Spinosaurus*, the largest meat-eating dinosaur, come from Morocco and Egypt.

The sail-backed *Ouranosaurus* is known from remains found in Niger.

▶ Janenschia *(Tanzania) was discovered in Africa during the 1990s.*

► In Africa, as elsewhere, fossils are easier to find in places with bare, rocky soils, such as the Sahara region.

Wawmda (Morroco)

Kem Kem Formation (Morroco)

Bahariya (Egypt)

In Gall (Niger)

Echkar Formation (Niger)

Gadoulfaoua (Niger)

Tendaguru (Tanzania)

Lake Kariba (Zimbabwe)

Kadzi (Zimbabwe)

Harrismith (South Africa)

Herschel (South Africa)

Ladybrand (South Africa)

Mafetang (South Africa)

- **Many sauropod fossils** were uncovered at African sites, including *Tornieri* from Tanzania, and *Vulcanodon* in Zimbabwe.

- **Remains of *Massospondylus*,** a plant-eating prosauropod, were extracted from several sites in southern Africa.

- **Fossils named as *Gyposaurus*** have been found in Orange Free State, South Africa.

- **During the 1908–12** fossil-hunting expedition to Tendaguru, more than 250 tonnes of fossil bones and rocks from dinosaurs such as *Giraffatitan* were carried 65 km to the nearest port, for transport to Germany.

Asia

- **Hundreds of kinds** of dinosaurs have been discovered on the continent of Asia.

- **In Asia**, most of the dinosaur fossils that have been found so far were located in the Gobi Desert in Central Asia, and in present-day China. Some were also found in present-day India.

- **Remains of *Titanosaurus***, the huge plant-eating sauropod, were uncovered near Umrer, in India. It lived about 70 mya, and was similar in shape to its cousin of the same time, *Saltasaurus*, from South America.

- ***Titanosaurus* was about** 12 m long and weighed 10–15 tonnes.

Gobi Desert (Mongolia)
Meileyingzi (China)
Jingangkon (China)
Taihezhen (China)
Wujiabai (China)
Lufeng (China)
Umrer (India)
Tiruchirapalli (India)

◀ Dinosaur fossil finds span the vast continent of Asia. (See later pages for more Gobi and China finds.)

▲ *The fossils of* Saltasaurus *(shown here) and* Titanosaurus *are very similar, and some experts consider them to be the same type of dinosaur.*

 Fossils of the sauropod *Barapasaurus* were found in India and described and named in 1975.

 ***Barapasaurus* was 14 m long** and probably weighed more than 10 tonnes. It is one of the first sauropods known from anywhere in the world, living around 190–180 mya.

Fossils of *Dravidosaurus*, once thought to belong to the stegosaur group, were found near Tiruchirapalli in southern India. Further studies suggest they are actually from a type of sea reptile.

Gobi Desert

- **The Gobi Desert** covers much of southern Mongolia and parts of northern China.

- **The first fossil-hunting expeditions** to the Gobi Desert took place in 1922–25, and were organized by the American Museum of Natural History.

- **The expeditions** set out to look for fossils of early humans, but instead found amazing dinosaur remains.

▼ Gallimimus *fossils were found in the early 1970s in the Nemegt region of the Gobi, which has yielded many exciting remains. There are parts of skeletons of many individuals, ranging from youngsters to adults.*

▶ The Gobi's fossil sites are far from any towns or cities. Searching for fossils is hard work in extreme temperatures and dust storms.

Gobi Desert (Mongolia)

'Flaming Cliffs'
Ömnögovi Province
Altan Ula
Toogreeg
Nemegt
Byan Dzak
Khulsan
Khermeen Tsav
Tsagan Kushu

 The first fossil dinosaur eggs were found by the 1922–25 expeditions.

 Velociraptor, Avimimus and *Pinacosaurus* were discovered in the Gobi.

 Russian expeditions to the Gobi Desert in 1946 and 1948–49 discovered new armoured and duckbilled dinosaurs.

 More expeditions in the 1960s–70s found the giant sauropod *Opisthocoelicaudia* and the helmet-headed *Prenocephale*.

 Other Gobi dinosaurs include *Gallimimus* and *Oviraptor*. In the 1990s–2000s more expeditions uncovered therizinosaurs.

China

- **For centuries**, dinosaur fossils in China were identified as belonging to folklore creatures such as dragons.

- **The first fossils** studied scientifically in China were uncovered in the 1930s.

- **From the 1980s**, dinosaur discoveries in almost every province of China have amazed scientists around the globe.

- **A few exciting dinosaur finds** in China have been fakes, such as part of a bird skeleton that was joined to the part-skeleton of a dinosaur along a natural-looking crack in the rock.

◀ Recent fossil finds in China are causing scientists to change many long-held ideas.

Liaoning

Jingangkon

Taihezhen

Wujiabai • Dashanpu

Lufeng

◀ When officially named in 2000, Microraptor, *from the Early Cretaceous Period, was the only dinosaur with feathers on its body, arms and legs.*

🦶 **Some better-known Chinese finds** include *Mamenchisaurus*, *Psittacosaurus*, *Tuojiangosaurus* and *Avimimus*.

🦶 **Remains of the prosauropod** *Lufengosaurus* were uncovered in China's southern province of Yunnan, in 1941.

DID YOU KNOW?
Only the USA probably has more fossil dinosaurs than China.

🦶 **China's *Lufengosaurus*** lived during the Early Jurassic Period, and measured about 6–7 m in length.

🦶 **Many recently found fossils** in China are of feathered dinosaurs such as *Caudipteryx*, *Sinosauropteryx* and *Microraptor*.

249

Australia

 In the past 50 years, some of the most exciting discoveries of dinosaur fossils have come from Australia.

Remains of the large plant-eater *Muttaburrasaurus* were found near Muttaburra, Queensland.

Muttaburrasaurus was about 8 m long and similar in some ways to the well known plant-eater *Iguanodon*.

Fossils of *Rhoetosaurus*, a giant plant-eater, were found in 1924 in southern Queensland.

DID YOU KNOW?
Dinosaur Cove is difficult to reach, and many of the fossils are in hard rocks in the middle of sheer cliffs with pounding waves far beneath.

▲ Muttaburrasaurus *lived 110–100 mya in what is now New South Wales, Australia. It could walk on two or four legs. A cousin of* Iguanodon, *it weighed 3 tonnes.*

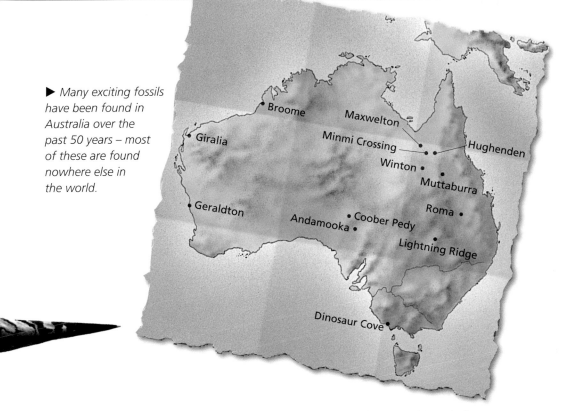

▶ Many exciting fossils have been found in Australia over the past 50 years – most of these are found nowhere else in the world.

Broome
Maxwelton
Giralia
Minmi Crossing
Hughenden
Winton
Muttaburra
Geraldton
Roma
Andamooka · Coober Pedy
Lightning Ridge
Dinosaur Cove

🐾 **The sauropod** *Rhoetosaurus* was about 15 m long and lived about 180–160 mya.

🐾 **Near Winton, Queensland**, more than 3300 footprints show where about 130 dinosaurs once passed by.

🐾 **One of the major fossil sites** in Australia is Dinosaur Cove, on the coast near Melbourne, Victoria.

🐾 **Fossil-rich rocks** at Dinosaur Cove are part of the Otway-Strzelecki mountain ranges, and are 120–110 million years old.

🐾 **Remains found** at Dinosaur Cove include *Leaellynasaura*, a smaller version of the huge meat-eater *Allosaurus*, and the 3-m, 120-kg plant-eater *Atlascopcosaurus*.

251

North America

🦖 **North America** is the continent where most dinosaur fossils have been found.

🦖 **Most of these fossils** come from the West region, which includes the US states of Montana, Wyoming, Utah, Colorado and Arizona and Alberta in Canada.

▲ *This map shows some of the most important fossil sites of North America. Remains of some of the most famous dinosaurs have been found at these locations, including* Allosaurus, Tyrannosaurus, Diplodocus, Triceratops *and* Stegosaurus.

▲ Coelophysis *was discovered in New Mexico, USA, in 1881. In the 1940s, another expedition found dozens of skeletons at a single site*

Several fossil-rich sites in North America are now national parks.

The US Dinosaur National Monument, on the border of Utah and Colorado, was established in 1915.

The Cleveland-Lloyd Dinosaur Quarry in Utah contains fossils of stegosaurs, ankylosaurs, sauropods and meat-eaters such as *Allosaurus*.

Along the Red Deer River in Alberta, a large area containing thousands of dinosaur fossils has been designated the Dinosaur Provincial Park.

Fossils found in Alberta include those of the meat-eater *Albertosaurus*, armoured *Euoplocephalus* and the duckbill *Lambeosaurus*.

The Dinosaur Provincial Park in Alberta is a United Nations World Heritage Site – an area of outstanding natural importance.

A huge, 20-m-long plant-eater was named *Alumosaurus* from the Ojo Alamo rock formations, now known as Kirtland Shales, in New Mexico, USA.

Dinosaur National Monument

🐾 **Dinosaur National Monument** is a protected area in the southwest of America, spanning the border between the states of Colorado and Utah.

🐾 **It was one of the first sites** in the world to be given special protection for having valuable fossils, back in 1915.

🐾 **Dinosaur National Monument today** covers more than 85,000 hectares.

🐾 **The rocks** at Dinosaur National Monument were originally the banks and bed of a river, where animal bodies were washed during floods, and preserved.

🐾 **The area contains** not only the fossil-rich Dinosaur Quarry, but also surrounding beautiful areas of the Uinta Mountains and the Yampa and Green Rivers.

🐾 **Today's harsh climate** at the Dinosaur National Monument area means many rocks are bare and wear away, or erode, to reveal thousands of fossils.

🐾 **Remains of more than 20 kinds** of dinosaurs and similar creatures have been found here, including the meat-eaters *Allosaurus* and *Ceratosaurus*.

▶ *A field worker carefully excavates fossil bones on a sloping rock layer at Dinosaur National Monument.*

There are also fossils of the 'ABCD' plant-eating sauropods *Apatosaurus*, *Barosaurus*, *Camarasaurus* and *Diplodocus*, and plate-backed *Stegosaurus*.

 Dinosaur National Monument receives up to half a million visitors each year.

At Dinosaur Wall in the Quarry visitor centre, people can see jumbled fossil bones and other remains sticking out of the rocks.

255

South America

 Many of the most important discoveries of dinosaur fossils in the last 30 years were made in South America.

 Dinosaur fossils have been found from the north to the south of the continent, in the countries of Brazil and Argentina.

 Most dinosaur fossils in South America have been found on the high grassland, scrub and semi-desert of southern Brazil and Argentina.

 Some of the earliest known dinosaurs, such as *Herrerasaurus* and *Eoraptor*, lived more than 225 mya in Argentina.

 Some of the last dinosaurs, such as the sauropods *Saltasaurus* and *Titanosaurus*, also lived in Argentina.

Fossils of the meat-eating predator *Piatnitzkysaurus* come from Cerro Condo in southern Argentina.

◄ Saltasaurus *is named after the region in Argentina where its fossils were discovered – Salta Province.*

▶ *Dinosaur fossils found in South America since the 1970s reveal unique kinds of meat-eaters, among the biggest predatory dinosaurs, some of the earliest members of the dinosaur group, and possibly the largest of all dinosaurs, Argentinosaurus.*

Boyacá
(Columbia)

Cerro Rajada
(Argentina)

El Breté (Argentina)

Santa Maria (Brazil)

Neuquén
(Argentina)

Ischigualasto
(Argentina)

Cerro Condor (Argentina)

Santa Cruz (Argentina)

DID YOU KNOW?

Some of the biggest dinosaurs, including the large meat-eater Giganotosaurus and the vast sauropod Argentinosaurus, come from Argentina.

🐾 **Piatnitzkysaurus was similar** to the great predator *Allosaurus* of North America, but at 4–5 m long, it was less than half its size.

🐾 **Like many dinosaurs in Argentina**, *Piatnitzkysaurus* lived during the Middle–Late Jurassic Period.

🐾 **Remains of about ten huge** *Patagosaurus* sauropods were found in the fossil-rich region of Chubut, Argentina, from 1977.

257

Antarctic dinosaurs

- **The huge continent of Antarctica** has not always been ice-covered at the South Pole.

- **Through parts of prehistory**, Antarctica was joined to Australia, and the climate was much warmer, allowing forests with trees and bushes to grow.

- **This happened** during the Early Jurassic Period, 201–174 mya, and again in the Early Cretaceous Period, 145–100 mya.

- **At this time**, insects, worms, reptiles such as dinosaurs and crocodiles and flying pterosaurs, mammals and many other creatures lived in Australia, and fossils of some have been found on Antarctica.

- **Finding fossils** on Antarctica is very difficult, with intense cold, bitter winds, blizzards, and rocks covered with ice and snow for most of the year.

- **The first dinosaur fossils** found on Antarctica were dug out in 1986 on James Ross Island, at the tip of the Antarctic Peninsula, south of South America.

- **The dinosaur**, of the ankylosaur or armoured dinosaur group, was named *Antarctopelta*, meaning 'Antarctic shield'.

- ***Antarctopelta* was about 4 m long**, weighed up to one tonne, and lived about 70 mya.

▶ Cryolophosaurus *fossils were found in the same region as those of sauropod dinosaurs, pterosaurs and therapsids (mammal-like reptiles) the size of rats.*

🦶 **The first discovery** of a meat-eating dinosaur on Antarctica was *Cryolophosaurus*, in 1991.

🦶 *Cryolophosaurus* **lived** during the Early Jurassic Period, some 190 mya. It was about 6 m long and weighed up to half a tonne.

🦶 **The name** *Cryolophosaurus* means 'frozen crest lizard' because this dinosaur had a bony crest that rose up between its eyes and had a comb-like tip.

Fossil formation

- **Most of the information we know**, or guess, about dinosaurs and other ancient life comes from fossils.

- **Fossils are the remains** of once-living things that have been preserved in rocks and turned to stone, usually over millions of years.

- **Many kinds of living things** from prehistoric times have left fossils, including mammals, birds, lizards, fish and insects as well as plants such as ferns and trees.

- **Using a dinosaur as an example of fossil formation**, the flesh, guts and other soft parts of the dead body were probably eaten by scavengers, or rotted away, so these parts rarely formed fossils.

▼ *Fossil formation is a very long process, and extremely prone to chance and luck. Only a tiny fraction of dinosaurs that ever lived have left remains preserved by this process. Because of the way fossils are formed, dinosaurs that died in water or along banks and shores were most likely to become fossilized. It is extremely rare to find all the parts of a dinosaur arranged as they were in life.*

1 Dinosaur dies and its soft parts are scavenged or rot away

2 Sand, mud or other sediments cover the hard parts, such as the claws, teeth or bones

Fossils usually formed when a dinosaur's remains were quickly covered by sediments such as sand, silt or mud, especially along the banks of a river or lake, or on the seashore.

 The sand or other sediment around a dinosaur's remains was gradually buried deeper by more sediment, squeezed under pressure, and cemented together into a solid mass of rock.

As the sediment turned to rock, so did the dinosaur remains encased within it.

Information about dinosaurs comes not only from fossils of their body parts, but also from 'trace' fossils. These were not actual parts of their bodies, but other items or signs of their presence.

 Trace fossils include egg shells, footprints, marks made by claws and teeth, and coprolites – fossilized dinosaur droppings.

3 More layers build up as the minerals in the bones and other hard parts turn to rock

4 Erosion (wearing away) of upper rock layers exposes the fossil, which is now solid stone

Age of Dinosaurs

- **The Age of Dinosaurs** corresponds to the time period that geologists call the Mesozoic Era, from about 252–66 mya.

- **The Mesozoic Era** is divided into three shorter time spans – the Triassic, Jurassic and Cretaceous Periods.

- **In the Triassic Period**, 252–201 mya, the dinosaurs began to evolve.

ERA	PERIOD	MYA
		— 70
		— 80
		— 90
	CRETACEOUS	— 100
	145–66 MYA	— 110
		— 120
		— 130
		— 140
MESOZOIC		— 150
		— 160
	JURASSIC	— 170
	201–145 MYA	— 180
		— 190
		— 200
		— 210
	TRIASSIC	— 220
	252–201 MYA	— 230
		— 240
		— 250

◄ *Dinosaurs ruled the land for 185 million years – longer than any other animal group.*

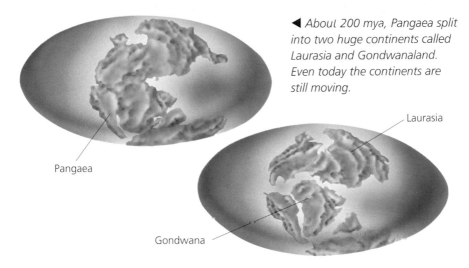

◀ *About 200 mya, Pangaea split into two huge continents called Laurasia and Gondwanaland. Even today the continents are still moving.*

Laurasia

Pangaea

Gondwana

🦶 **During the Jurassic Period** – about 201–145 mya – many dinosaurs reached their greatest size.

🦶 **The Cretaceous Period** is when dinosaurs were at their most varied - about 145–66 mya.

🦶 **All through the Mesozoic Era**, and before and since, the major landmasses gradually moved across the globe in a process known as continental drift.

🦶 **In the Triassic Period**, all the continents were joined as one supercontinent – Pangaea.

🦶 **In the Jurassic Period**, Pangaea separated into two huge landmasses – Laurasia in the north and Gondwana in the south.

🦶 **In the Cretaceous Period**, Laurasia and Gondwana split, and the continents began to take the positions we know now.

🦶 **The joining and separating** of the continents affected which kinds of dinosaurs lived where.

Archosaurs

- **Archosaurs were a large group** of reptiles that included the dinosaurs as one of their subgroups.

- **Other archosaur subgroups** included flying pterosaurs, crocodiles, and birds – since birds evolved from dinosaurs.

- **Pseudosuchians are living crocodilians** as were the lesser-known reptile group, the ornithosuchians, which were closely related to them but are now all extinct.

- **A dinosaur-like ornithosuchian** was *Ornithosuchus*, which gave its name to this group.

- **Four-metre-long** *Ornithosuchus* could stand almost upright and was probably a powerful predator.

- ***Ornithosuchus* fossils** have been found in Scotland.

▼ Ornithosuchus *had a mix of features, both non-dinosaur (hips and back plates) and dinosaur (legs and skull).*

🐾 **Features in *Ornithosuchus'*** backbone, hips and feet indicate that it was not quite a dinosaur, but still an archosaur.

🐾 **Some experts classify** *Archosaurus* from the Permian Period as one of the first archosaurs, while others disagree.

◄ *Crocodilians, like this hatchling, are living members of the great archosaur group of reptiles.*

265

Inventing the dinosaur

- **When fossils of dinosaurs** were first studied by scientists in the 1820s, they were thought to be from huge lizards, rhinoceroses or even whales.

- **The first dinosaur** to be officially named in 1824 was *Megalosaurus*, by Englishman William Buckland.

- **Fossils of dinosaurs** were found and studied in 1822 by Gideon Mantell, a doctor in Sussex, southern England.

- **In 1825**, Mantell named the creature *Iguanodon*, because its teeth were very similar in shape to, but larger than, the teeth of the iguana lizard.

- **In the late 1830s**, British scientist Richard Owen realized that some fossils did not belong to lizards, but to an as yet unnamed group of reptiles.

- **In 1841–42**, Richard Owen invented a new name for the group of giant prehistoric reptiles – Dinosauria.

- **The name 'dinosaur'** means 'terrible lizard/reptile'.

- **Life-sized models** of several dinosaurs were made by British sculptor Waterhouse Hawkins in 1852–54.

- **Hawkins' models** were displayed at the Crystal Palace Exhibition in London, and caused a public sensation.

▼ Megalosaurus *was the first dinosaur to be given an official scientific name, even though the term 'dinosaur' had not yet been invented.*

DID YOU KNOW?

The three main dinosaurs of the newly named Dinosauria in the 1840s were Iguanodon, meat-eater Megalosaurus and the nodosaur Hylaeosaurus.

Dinosaur fossil hunters

- **Many dinosaurs** were found in the USA in the 1870s–90s by Othniel Charles Marsh and Edward Drinker Cope.

- **Marsh and Cope** were great rivals, each one trying to find bigger, better and more dinosaur fossils than the other.

- **Between 1877 and 1897**, Cope and Marsh found and described about 130 new kinds of dinosaurs.

- **Joseph Tyrrell** discovered fossils of *Albertosaurus* in 1884, in what became a very famous dinosaur region, the Red Deer River area of Alberta, Canada.

- **Lawrence Lambe** found many North American dinosaur fossils, such as *Centrosaurus* in 1904.

- **German fossil experts** Werner Janensch and Edwin Hennig led expeditions to east Africa in 1908–12, and discovered *Giraffatitan* and *Kentrosaurus*.

- **From 1933**, Yang Zhong-jiang (also called CC Young) led many fossil hunting expeditions in China.

- **José Bonaparte** from Argentina has found many fossils in that region, including *Carnotaurus* in 1985.

- **Paul Sereno** from the University of Chicago has discovered and named huge dinosaurs and crocodiles from South America and North Africa.

DID YOU KNOW?
One of the first great fossil hunters in the USA was Joseph Leidy, who found Troodon in 1856.

◄ ▼ *Othniel Charles Marsh and Edward Drinker Cope had a rivalry between them that came to be known as the 'Bone Wars'. Allegedly, this began when Marsh pointed out a mistake that Cope had made with the reconstruction of a plesiosaur skeleton. Cope never forgave him, but the rift led to the discovery of almost 140 new dinosaur species.*

Othniel Charles Marsh
(1831–99)

Edward Drinker Cope
(1840–97)

Dinosaur names 1

 Every dinosaur has a scientific name, usually made up from Latin or Greek, place names or person names, and written in *italics*.

 Many dinosaur names end in *-saurus*, which some scientists say means 'reptile' and others say means 'lizard' – but dinosaurs were not lizards.

 Names often refer to a unique feature a dinosaur had. *Baryonyx*, for example, means 'heavy claw', from the massive claw on its thumb.

 Many dinosaur names are real tongue-twisters, such as *Opisthocoelicaudia*, pronounced 'owe-pis-thowe-see-lee-cord-ee-ah'. The name means 'posterior tail cavity', and refers to the joints between the backbones in the dinosaur's tail.

 Some dinosaurs are named after the place where their fossils were found. *Minmi* was found near Minmi Crossing, Queensland, Australia.

 The fast-running ostrich dinosaurs are named ornithomimosaurs, which means 'bird-mimic reptiles'.

▶ *In 1988, an almost complete specimen of the meat-eater* Herrerasaurus *was excavated in Argentina. It was named after Victorino Herrera, the farmer who discovered it.*

DID YOU KNOW?

Some dinosaur groups are named after the first discovered or major one of its kind, such as the tyrannosaurs or stegosaurs.

Dinosaur names 2

 More than 150 types of dinosaur have been named after the people who first discovered their fossils, dug them up, or reconstructed the dinosaur.

The large duckbill (hadrosaur) *Lambeosaurus* was named after Canadian fossil expert Lawrence Lambe.

Lambe worked mainly during the early 1900s, and named one of his finds *Stephanosaurus*.

In the 1920s, *Stephanosaurus* was renamed, along with *Didanodon*, as *Lambeosaurus*, in honour of Lambe's work.

The full name of the 'heavy claw' meat-eater *Baryonyx* is *Baryonyx walkeri*, after Bill Walker, the discoverer of its massive claw.

Part-time fossil hunter Bill Walker found the claw in a clay pit quarry in Surrey, England.

◀ *The first fossil find of Baryonyx was its huge thumb claw.*

▶ Alectrosaurus *means 'lonely lizard'. It lived 80–75 mya in Central Asia.*

 Some dinosaur names are quite technical, such as *Diplodocus*, which means 'double beam'. It was named for its tail bones, which have two long projections like a pair of skis.

 The 4-m-long plant-eater *Othnielia* was named after 19th-century fossil hunter Othniel Charles Marsh.

 Parksosaurus, a 2.5-m-long plant-eater, was named in honour of Canadian dinosaur expert William Parks.

DID YOU KNOW?
One of the shortest dinosaur names is Kol, a tiny meat-eater known from only one fossil foot.

Reconstructions

- **No complete fossilized dinosaur**, with its skin, muscles, guts and other soft body parts, has ever been found.

- **Most dinosaurs are reconstructed** from the fossils of their teeth, bones, horns and claws.

- **The vast majority** are known from only a few fossil parts, such as several fragments of bones.

- **Fossil parts** of other, similar dinosaurs are often used in reconstructions to 'fill in' missing bones, teeth, and even missing heads, limbs or tails.

- **Soft body parts** from modern reptiles, such as lizards, are used as a guide for the reconstruction of a dinosaur's muscles and guts.

- **On rare occasions**, remains are found of a dinosaur body that dried out rapidly so that quite a few parts were preserved as mummified fossils.

- **One of the best known** of the best-preserved dinosaur fossils is of *Brachylophosaurus*, a 9-m hadrosaur (duck-bill) from about 75 mya.

▶ *This fossil skeleton of an ankylosaur,* Euoplocephalus, *has been restored with soft parts inside, then muscles and finally the skin covering with scales and horns.*

Nicknamed 'Elvis', this amazing fossil was discovered in 1994 by fossil hunter Nate Murphy in Montana.

 In 2000 Murphy found an even better *Brachylophosaurus*, which was called 'Leonardo'.

Age of mammals

Bird fossils

 There are far fewer fossils of birds than other animals because birds have very delicate skeletons.

 Some species of prehistoric birds are only revealed by the fossil impression of a feather or a fossilized footprint.

 One of the most famous bird fossils is that of *Archaeopteryx*, which was discovered in Solnhofen, Germany, in 1861.

 Lime-rich muds slowly formed the limestone rock of Solnhofen. This process ensured *Archaeopteryx* was preserved in amazing detail, right down to the clear outline of its feathers.

 Other famous bird fossil sites have included the Niobrara Chalk of Kansas, and mudstone rocks of Utah and Wyoming.

 The fossil site at Messel in Germany also contains the skeletons of long-extinct birds as well as ones resembling flamingos, swifts, owls and nightjars.

 The Messel bird fossils are around 47 million years old and date from the Middle Paleogene Period.

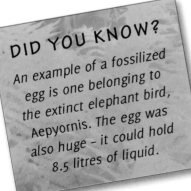

DID YOU KNOW?
An example of a fossilized egg is one belonging to the extinct elephant bird, *Aepyornis*. The egg was also huge – it could hold 8.5 litres of liquid.

 Flamingo fossils at Messel proved that the modern flamingo is related to wading birds called avocets rather than ducks and storks, since they share a similar skeleton.

 One quick way fossil hunters can identify bird bones is because they are hollow – unlike the bones of many prehistoric reptiles.

▲ *Fossils of* Archaeopteryx *are some of the most famous fossils of all. They show the bird's feathers, clawed fingers, teeth-filled beak and long tail.*

Terror birds

🦶 **After the large dinosaurs** became extinct (about 66 mya), huge flightless birds – known as terror birds – seized the opportunity to become the dominant predators of their day.

🦶 *Gastornis* **was one** such terror bird. It had an enormous head and powerful legs, like those of its dinosaur ancestors, so it could outrun its prey.

🦶 **Some experts believe** that *Gastornis* is a close cousin of ducks, geese and other related birds.

🦶 **Even though these birds** were huge, they were also light-footed, fast runners. This is because, like all birds, they had hollow bones.

🦶 **The diets of terror birds** included small and medium-sized mammals, such as prehistoric rodents and horses.

🦶 **During the Late Eocene** and Oligocene Epochs (40–23 mya), the big carnivorous mammals became more powerful and better hunters. They became dominant, and took over.

🦶 **However, in South America**, which was cut off from North America and the rest of the world for much of the past 66 million years, terror birds managed to stay dominant for a longer period of time.

🦶 **One South American terror bird** was *Phorusrhacus*, which grew to be 2.5 m tall.

🦶 *Titanis* **was one** of the few North American terror birds, and one of the biggest of all – it was 2.5 m tall and weighed 150 kg.

▶ Gastornis *attacks a small mammal of its time*, Leptictidium.

DID YOU KNOW?

Gastornis was named in 1855 after Gaston Planté, a fossil-hunter who turned to physics, and four years later invented the lead-acid battery used in cars and trucks.

281

Other flightless birds

- **Most prehistoric flightless birds** were giants, but not all of them were terror birds.

- **Much later giant birds** grew to incredible sizes. *Dinornis*, for instance, was the tallest flightless bird ever at 3.5 m tall.

- *Dinornis* **lived** in New Zealand. It first appeared about 2 mya and survived until perhaps 500 years ago!

- *Dinornis* **was one of a group** of birds known as moas. At various times there were probably about eight or nine different kinds of moas living on the two main islands of New Zealand.

- **The largest kinds of** *Dinornis* were the giant moas, which were extremely heavy, weighing over 200 kg.

- **The disappearance of the moas** was soon after humans reached New Zealand, and all moas were probably extinct by the end of the 15th century.

- **Another group** of enormous flightless birds lived on the island of Madagascar, and were called elephant birds.

- **At 450 kg**, the giant elephant bird *Aepyornis* was probably the heaviest bird ever to have lived. Like moas, the elephant birds became extinct within the last 500 years.

- **Both *Dinornis* and *Aepyornis*** were herbivores. Their diet consisted of seeds and fruit.

DID YOU KNOW?
Genetic studies show the closest living relative of moas is probably the ostrich of Africa.

◀ On Madagascar, in the absence of large mammal grazers and browsers, elephant birds evolved to become the biggest land herbivores.

Water birds

- *Ichthyornis* **was a prehistoric seagull**, which first appeared in the Late Cretaceous Period (100–66 mya).

- **It was similar in size** to a modern seagull, but had a much larger head and a beak full of very sharp teeth.

- *Presbyornis* **was related** to modern ducks. Like *Ichthyornis*, it evolved in the Late Cretaceous Period and was abundant in the Early Paleogene Period (66–40 mya).

- *Presbyornis* **was much bigger** than a modern duck – it stood between 0.5 m and one metre tall.

- **It had much longer legs** than its modern relative and so may have been a wading bird rather than a diving bird.

- *Presbyornis* **lived in large flocks** on lake shores, like modern flamingos.

- *Osteodontornis* **was a huge flying bird**, with a wingspan up to 6 m across.

- **It lived in the Miocene Epoch** (23–5 mya) and would have flown over the North Pacific Ocean.

- *Osteodontornis* **had a long bill**, lined with tooth-like bony spikes. Its diet probably included squid, seized from the surface of the sea.

▶ *Osteodontornis* was in the bird group called pseudotooths, where the 'teeth' were small bony points or spikes growing from the jaw bones, rather than true teeth.

DID YOU KNOW?

The skull of Presbyornis most closely resembles that of the living Australian duck Stictonetta.

Land birds

- **Land birds are flying birds** that fly in the skies over land and hunt or feed on the ground, unlike water birds.

- **Fossils of prehistoric land birds** are rare because their bones were light and would not have fossilized well.

- **As a result**, there are big gaps in palaeontologists' knowledge of the evolution of many species of birds. However, there are some early land birds they do know about.

- *Archaeopsittacus* **was an early parrot** of the Late Oligocene Epoch (28–23 mya) that lived in what is now France.

- *Ogygoptynx* **was one of** the first known owls. It lived in the Palaeocene Epoch (66–56 mya).

- *Aegialornis* **was an early** swift-like bird, which lived in the Eocene and Oligocene Epochs (56–23 mya). It may be the ancestor of swifts and hummingbirds.

- *Gallinuloides* **was an early member** of the chicken family. Its fossils have been found in Wyoming, USA, in rock strata of the Eocene Epoch (56–33 mya).

- **The earliest known vultures** lived in the Palaeocene Epoch (66–56 mya).

- **The earliest known hawks**, cranes, bustards, cuckoos and songbirds lived in the Eocene Epoch.

▶ *Vultures have been following the same scavenging way of life for more than 50 million years.*

DID YOU KNOW?

Neocathartes was an early vulture-like bird. There are similarities between its skeleton and those of storks, which suggests vultures and storks are closely related.

Mammal fossils

◄ *Fur is still visible around the feet of Dima, the well preserved remains of a baby mammoth.*

 Fossil finds of prehistoric mammals include skulls, teeth, jawbones, ear bones, horns, tusks and antlers.

There are few fossils of the earliest mammals because scavengers would usually have eaten their bodies.

However, coprolites (fossilized dung) of predators and scavengers sometimes contain undigested parts of the early mammals themselves, such as their teeth.

Palaeontologists can tell a lot from a mammal's molars (cheek teeth). They can work out its species and the period it lived in from the pattern of ridges and furrows on their surface.

Palaeontologists can also estimate the age of a mammal when it died by looking at the wear and tear on its teeth.

Some mammal fossils are preserved in tar pits – natural pools of thick, sticky tar, which ooze up from the ground in some places, such as forests and scrublands.

Tar pits at Rancho La Brea, near present-day downtown Los Angeles, USA, contained a perfectly preserved skeleton of the sabre-tooth carnivore *Smilodon*.

▲ *This enormous mammoth skull was found in South Dakota, USA. In Siberia, palaeontologists have also discovered the remains of mammoth skin, hair and other body parts.*

 Freezing is another very effective way of preserving animals. Remains of frozen mammoths have been discovered in near-perfect condition in Siberia.

 Explorers using dog sledges discovered some of the first frozen mammoths. Their remains were so well preserved that the dogs were able to eat the meat on the bones.

 In 1977, an almost complete mammoth was discovered. 'Dima' is the name given to the frozen 40,000-year-old baby mammoth.

Mammal offspring

- **Mammals developed a very different way** of producing young, compared to reptiles and birds, which both lay eggs.

- **Instead, most mammals** are viviparous, which means they give birth to live young.

- **One unusual group of mammals**, the monotremes, defy this rule by laying eggs. There are five surviving monotremes – the duck-billed platypus and four species of echidna.

- **After the young of mammals are born**, their mothers feed them milk that is produced in their mammary glands.

- **The word 'mammal'** comes from the name for the mammary glands – the part of female mammals' bodies that secretes milk.

- **Early mammals**, such as *Megazostrodon*, *Eozostrodon* and *Morganucodon*, grew one set of milk teeth, which suggests that the young fed on milk.

- **Milk teeth** are temporary teeth that grow with the nutrients provided by milk, and prepare the jaw for later teeth.

- **Mammals can be divided** into three groups depending on how they rear their young – placentals, marsupials and monotremes.

- **In placental mammals**, the offspring grows inside its mother's body, in the womb, until it is a fully developed baby – at which point it is born.

- **Marsupial mammals** give birth to their offspring at a much earlier stage. The tiny infants then develop fully in their mothers' pouch, called a marsupium.

▼ Mammal mothers care for their young, as with Toxodon, which lived in South America as recently as 20,000 years ago.

Early mammals

- *Megazostrodon* was one of the first true mammals. It appeared at the start of the Early Jurassic Period (about 200 mya).

- **This shrew-like insectivore** (insect-eater) was about 12 cm long. It had a long body that was low to the ground, and long limbs that it held out to the side in a squatting position.

- *Eozostrodon* was another very early mammal, which emerged about the same time as *Megazostrodon*.

- **It had true mammalian teeth**, including two different sorts of cheek teeth – premolars and molars – which were replaced only once during its lifetime.

- **Its sharp teeth** suggest it was a meat-eater, and its large eyes suggest that it hunted at night.

- **Another early mammal** was *Morganucodon*. It too had premolars and molars and chewed its food in a circular motion, rather than the up-down motion of reptiles.

- *Sinoconodon* was yet another early mammal that lived in the Early Jurassic Period, about 190 mya. It was probably covered in fur.

- **These early mammals** had three middle ear bones, which made their hearing more sensitive than that of reptiles.

- **They also had whiskers**, which suggests they had fur. This in turn suggests that they were warm-blooded.

- **All true mammals** are warm-blooded, which means they maintain a constant body temperature. Fur helps mammals keep warm in cold conditions.

▼ Among the best-preserved fossil mammals is Leptictidium from Germany's Messel Pit site, at 45 million years of age.

Marsupials

Marsupials are mammals that give birth to their offspring at a very early stage in their development – when they are still tiny.

After being born, the infant crawls through its mother's fur to a pouch called the marsupium, where it stays, feeding on milk, until it is big enough to leave.

Palaeontologists think that the first marsupials evolved in Asia and then spread to the Americas and Australia.

An early marsupial called *Alphadon,* meaning 'first tooth', emerged around 70 mya. It lived in North America.

Alphadon **was 30 cm long** and weighed 300 g. It would have lived in trees, using its feet to climb, and fed on insects, fruit and small vertebrates.

When Australia became isolated from the rest of the world, about 40 mya, its marsupials continued to evolve – unlike most other regions of the world, where they fell into decline.

Marsupials continued to exist in South America, which was also isolated from the rest of the world during much of the last 66 million years, the Paleogene and Neogene Periods.

When South America became reconnected with North America, from about 4 mya, the arrival of placental mammals from the north led many marsupials to extinction.

Today, there are only two surviving groups of marsupials in the Americas – the opossums found throughout North America and the rat opossums found in South America.

Australia has many living marsupials, such as kangaroos and koalas. However it had a much greater marsupial population in the Paleogene and Neogene Periods – we know this from fossil sites such as Riversleigh in northwest Queensland.

▼ Thylacoleo, *the 'marsupial lion', was similar to a modern small puma (mountain lion), but with huge slashing thumb claws. Its remains have been discovered in Australia.*

Australian mammals

- **Australia has a unique natural history** because it became isolated from the rest of the world around 40 mya.

- **Australia's native mammals**, living and extinct, are mostly marsupials – mammals that give birth to tiny young, which then develop in their mother's outside pouch.

- **The earliest Australian marsupials** date from the Oligocene Epoch (34–23 mya). Many fossils come from the Miocene Epoch (23–5 mya) or later.

- **These fossils show** that there were giant kangaroos, called *Procoptodon*, as well as giant wombats, called *Diprotodon*.

- **Two marsupial carnivores** preyed on these giant herbivores. One was the lion-like *Thylacoleo*, the other was the smaller, wolf-like *Thylacinus*.

- **Palaeontologists** are very interested in *Thylacoleo* and *Thylacinus* because they demonstrate how different species can evolve to look very similar – the process known as evolutionary convergence.

- **Although they had different ancestors** and lived on different continents, *Thylacoleo* came to look like a placental lion, while *Thylacinus* came to look like a placental wolf.

- **The Miocene fossil site** in Riversleigh, northern Queensland, has revealed the extent and variety of prehistoric marsupials in Australia.

Among the fossils are many long-extinct marsupials. One of these was so unusual that at first palaeontologists called it a 'thingodont', although now it is known as *Yalkaparidon*.

 Thylacinus **continued** to exist in Australia into the 20th century, as the thylacine. The last one died in a zoo in Tasmania in 1936.

◀ *At 3 m long, the giant wombat* Diprotodon *was probably the largest marsupial ever to have lived. It had tusks for its front teeth, but its cheek teeth were like a kangaroo's.*

South American mammals

- **South America was separated** from the rest of the world for much of the last 60 million years.

- **Like Australia**, South America's isolation meant that certain mammals only evolved there.

- **The main difference** between them was that South America had placental mammals as well as marsupials.

- **Placental mammals** included the giant ground sloths, such as *Megatherium*, and huge rodents the size of bears.

- **Marsupial mammals** included the marsupial carnivores, such as *Thylacosmilus*.

- **Evolutionary convergence**, when different species develop to look very similar, happened in South America just as in Australia. One example was *Thoatherium*, which looked very much like the small horses that were evolving in other parts of the world.

- **The formation** of the Panama isthmus (a strip of land) reconnected South America to North America from about 4 mya.

DID YOU KNOW?

A good example of evolutionary convergence was Pyrotherium, which had the trunk, cheek teeth and tusks of an early elephant – but it belonged to a different group.

Many South American mammals journeyed north. Some, such as armadillos, porcupines and guinea pigs, were very successful in their new homes.

 Others, like the glyptodonts, eventually died out. This might be because of climate change – or because humans hunted them to extinction.

▼ *The South American hoofed mammal known as* Macrauchenia *used its short trunk to gather vegetation. It lived from about 6 million to 30,000 years ago.*

299

Creodonts

- **Creodonts were the first** big flesh-eating mammals. They lived from the Paleocene to the Miocene Epochs (about 50–10 mya).

- **These mammals came** in many different shapes and sizes. Some were as small as weasels, others were bigger than bears.

- **Many creodonts** were flat-footed and walked on short, heavy limbs tipped with claws.

- **They hunted early herbivores** that, like these early carnivores, had not yet evolved into quick runners.

- **Creodonts had smaller**, more primitive brains than later carnivores – these were cleverer, faster hunters than the creodonts, and forced them into decline.

- **Another way** in which creodonts were less successful than later carnivores was their teeth, which were less effective at stabbing or slicing.

- **Creodonts were**, however, the top predators of their day. The wolf-sized *Hyaenodon* was particularly successful.

DID YOU KNOW?
Hyaenodon species ranged in size from 30 cm high at the shoulders to 1.2 m high – the size of a small rhinoceros.

- **Fossils of *Hyaenodon* skulls** show that they had a very highly developed sense of smell, as well as powerful, bone-crushing jaws.

- **Fossils of male *Hyaenodon*** teeth reveal grinding marks, which palaeontologists think means they ground their teeth to ward off rivals, like some modern animals.

▲ Hyaenodon *fossils are known from many regions including Europe, Asia, Africa and North America.*

Carnivores

- **The first carnivorous mammals** were the creodonts, which ranged in size from the cat-like *Oxyaena* to the wolf-like *Mesonyx*.

- **In the Late Eocene Epoch** (around 40 mya) large hoofed carnivores, such as *Andrewsarchus*, began to appear.

- **Modern carnivores** are descended from a separate group called miacids.

- **Modern carnivores** belong to the order Carnivora. This order had two subgroups – the feliforms, which include the cats, and the caniforms – the dog families and the pinnipeds (seals, sea lions and walruses). Some classification schemes put pinnipeds in their own mammal group, separate from the other carnivores.

- **In the Oligocene Epoch** (34–23 mya), carnivorans began to replace creodonts as the dominant carnivores.

- **Carnivorans were smarter**, faster, and deadlier than creodonts, and were the only predators that could catch the new fast-running herbivores.

DID YOU KNOW?

The pinniped *Allodesmus* was a prehistoric seal. It had flippers, large eyes and spiky teeth, which it used to impale fish.

- **Faster mammals** evolved in the Oligocene Epoch as thick forests changed into open woodlands, with more space to run after, and run from, other creatures.

As carnivorans evolved they developed bigger brains, more alert senses, sharper claws and teeth, and stronger jaws and limbs.

 The pinnipeds are carnivorous mammals that, like whales and dolphins (and reptiles before them), reinvaded the seas.

▼ Andrewsarchus *is known only from a fossil skull, which suggests a huge beast with a head-body length of 3.5 m, a shoulder height of 1.7 m and a weight approaching one tonne.*

Cats

🐾 **The most highly developed** carnivores are cats. They are the fastest hunters, with the greatest agility, and with the sharpest claws and teeth.

🐾 **Cats evolved** along two lines. One group included the various kinds of sabre-tooths, of which *Smilodon* was one. This group is extinct today.

🐾 **Sabre-tooths** probably specialized in killing large, heavily built animals with thick hides, which explains their long canine teeth.

🐾 **The other group** of cats is the felines, which are the ancestors of all modern cats, from lions and cheetahs to pet cats.

▼ Dinofelis *was a muscular, heavily built predator with relatively short canines for a sabre-tooth cat.*

- **The felines were faster** and more agile than the sabre-tooths, which may have become extinct because their prey became faster and more able to outrun them. The felines, however, continued to be successful hunters.

- **One prehistoric feline** was *Dinictis*, a puma-sized cat that lived in the Oligocene Epoch (37–23 mya).

- **Later felines** were various types of *Dinofelis*, which lived between 5 and 1.3 mya across North America, Europe, Africa and Asia.

- **The name *Dinofelis*** means 'terrible cat'. It looked like a modern jaguar, but had stronger front legs that it used to press down on its victims before stabbing them with its teeth.

- ***Dinofelis'* diet** included baboons, antelope and perhaps australopithecines – our prehistoric human relatives.

DID YOU KNOW?

Prehistoric cats' ability to unsheathe and retract their claws provided them with one of their deadliest weapons – and one that cats still have.

305

Dogs

 Early dogs probably hunted in a similar way to most modern wild dogs – in packs.

 Dogs developed long snouts, which gave them a keen sense of smell, and forward-pointing eyes, which gave them good vision.

Dogs also developed a mixture of teeth – sharp canines for stabbing, narrow cheek teeth for slicing, and farther along the jaw at the back, flatter teeth for crushing.

These different teeth meant that dogs could eat a variety of different foods, including plants, which they might have had to eat if meat was in short supply.

One of the ancestors of dogs, as well as bears, was the bear-dog *Amphicyon*. Its name means 'in-between dog'.

Amphicyon **lived** between 20 and 10 mya.

Trace fossils of *Amphicyon's* footprints show that it walked like a bear, with its feet flat on the ground.

 Hesperocyon was one of the earliest dogs, living between about 40 and 30 mya.

Hesperocyon was the size of a small fox. It had long legs and jaws, forward-pointing eyes and a supple, slender body.

DID YOU KNOW?

Hunting in packs allowed Hesperocyon to catch large animals that it would not have been able to kill on its own.

▶ *In North America a pack-leading, or alpha-male,* Hesperocyon *tackles an extinct relative of deer,* Synthetoceras.

Herbivores

- **The first specialist herbivores** (plant-eaters) appeared in the Late Palaeocene Epoch (around 60 mya).

- **They ranged in size** from the equivalent of modern badgers to pigs.

- **These early herbivores** were rooters or browsers – they foraged for food on the floor or among branches in their forest homes.

- **It was not until** the very end of the Palaeocene Epoch (56 mya) that the first large herbivores evolved.

- **Large herbivores** emerged before large carnivores. They must have had a peaceful life – for a while.

- *Uintatherium* **was one** of the large early herbivores. It was the size of a large rhinoceros, with thick limbs to support its heavy body.

- *Uintatherium* **had three pairs** of bony knobs protruding from its head. Males had very long, strong canine teeth, which they would have used if attacked by creodont carnivores.

- **The growth of grasslands** and the decline of forests in the Miocene Epoch (23–5 mya) sped up changes to herbivores' bodies.

- **Herbivores developed** faster legs to outrun carnivores in open spaces. They also developed better digestive systems to cope with the new, tough grasses.

- **The most important** requirements for a herbivore are complex teeth and digestive systems to break down plant food and release its energy.

▼ *Elasmotherium* was a huge rhinoceros, about the size of modern elephants, that lived 2–1 mya in Europe and Asia.

Rodents

 In terms of their numbers, variety and distribution, rodents are the most successful mammals that have ever lived.

Squirrels, **rats, guinea pigs**, beavers, porcupines, voles, gophers and mice are all types of rodent.

Rodents have been – and still are – so successful because they are small, fast-breeding and able to digest all kinds of foods, including substances as hard as wood.

One of the first known rodents was *Paramys*, which appeared more than 50 mya.

Paramys **was a squirrel-like rodent** that could climb trees. It was 60 cm long, and had a long, slightly bushy tail.

Modern squirrels evolved around 40 mya. These mammals have one of the longest known ancestries for any living mammal group.

Another early rodent was *Epigaulus*, which was a gopher with two horns. The horns were side by side on the top of its snout, pointing upward.

DID YOU KNOW?

Rabbits and hares are descended from rodents. Modern hares first appeared around 5 mya.

Epigaulus **was 30 cm long** and lived in North America in the Miocene Epoch (23–5 mya). It probably used its horns for defence or digging up roots.

Prehistoric rodents could be massive. *Castoroides* was an early beaver that was over 2 m long – almost the size of a black bear.

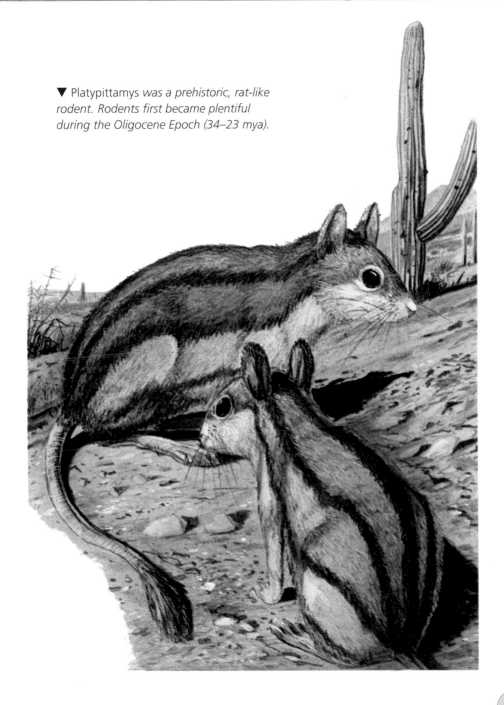

▼ Platypittamys *was a prehistoric, rat-like rodent. Rodents first became plentiful during the Oligocene Epoch (34–23 mya).*

Ruminants

- **Ruminants are a successful group** of plant-eating mammals that first appeared about 40 mya.

- **Modern ruminants** include cattle, sheep, deer, giraffes, antelopes and camels.

- **All these animals** can eat quickly, store plant material in the stomach, and then bring it back to their mouths again to chew it and break it down. This process is called 'chewing the cud'.

- *Archaeomeryx* **was an early**, rat-to-rabbit-sized ruminant, which lived in Asia. It was similar to the living chevrotain – a small, hoofed mammal also known as the mouse deer.

- *Archaeomeryx* **probably** had a three-chambered stomach, each of which broke down its plant food a little bit further.

- **Camels were the next** ruminants to evolve. One large prehistoric camel was *Aepycamelus*, which had a very long, giraffe-like neck.

- **They were followed** by cattle, sheep and deer, which were more advanced ruminants because they had four-chambered stomachs.

- **The four chambers** of ruminants' stomachs are called the rumen, the reticulum, the omasum and the abosmasum.

- **Ruminants' big advantage** over other plant-eaters was that they could decide when to digest their food. If they sensed a threat while they were eating they could run away and digest their meal later.

- **Camels and chevrotains** are the only surviving ruminants with three-chambered stomachs.

◀ Aepycamelus *was a large, giraffe-like prehistoric camel found in Colorado, North America, during the Miocene Epoch, 23–5 mya.*

Condylarths

- **Condylarths were among** the first hoofed mammals.

- **They lived in** the Paleogene Period, 66–23 mya.

- **All later hoofed mammals**, from horses to pigs, are probably descended from condylarths or similar animals.

- **The earliest condylarths** had claws as opposed to hooves.

- **Later species evolved** longer limbs, tipped with nails or hooves, for running away quickly from carnivores.

- **The first known condylarth** was *Protungulatum*, a rabbit-sized plant-eater, living 64–63 mya.

- **A slightly later condylarth** was *Phenacodus*, which palaeontologists think was an insectivore (an insect-eater).

- *Phenacodus* **was the size** of a small sheep, and had clearly developed hooves.

- **Condylarths spread** over most of the world, including Europe, Asia, South America and Africa.

DID YOU KNOW?

Early condylarths were also rabbit-sized. Later ones, however, were as big as bears.

▼ Arctocyon, *from about 50 mya, was probably 2 m long from head to tail. Muscle marks on fossils suggest it could climb trees.*

Perissodactyls

- **Perissodactyls are plant-eating**, hoofed mammals with an odd number of toes (either three or one) on their feet.

- **The three living groups** of perissodactyls are horses, tapirs and rhinoceroses.

▼ *One branch of the rhinoceros family developed to be enormous animals. They roamed across Asia, browsing leaves and twigs from treetops. The biggest of these was* Paraceratherium, *the largest land mammal ever.*

Two extinct groups of perissodactyls are brontotheres and chalicotheres.

Brontotheres included massive beasts, such as *Brontotherium*, which had elephant-like limbs and a blunt, bony prong jutting from its nose. It ate only soft-leaved plants.

 Chalicotherium was a chalicothere. It lacked front teeth, and ate by placing soft plant shoots in the back of its mouth, like a modern panda.

The earliest ancestors of modern horses, tapirs and rhinos, appeared before 50 mya, probably as the Paleocene Epoch gave way to the Eocene, 56 mya.

Miotapirus **was an early type** of tapir. It lived in North America about 20 mya and was similar in size to living tapirs, 1.5–2 m long.

Perissodactyls' feet carried the weight of the animal on the middle toe, either in a single hoof, as in horses, or a big toe with one on each side, as in tapirs and rhinos.

For much of the Paleogene Period (66–23 mya), perissodactyls were the most abundant form of hoofed mammals. They then declined, however, and artiodactyls (even-toed mammals) became dominant.

317

Artiodactyls

- **Artiodactyls are hoofed mammals** with an even number (either two or four) of toes on their feet.

- **Pigs, camels, giraffes**, sheep, goats, cattle, hippopotamuses, deer, antelopes and their ancestors are all artiodactyls.

- **Like the perissodactyls**, artiodactyls first appeared about 55–50 mya.

- *Dichobune* **was an early artiodactyl**, which lived between 40 and 30 mya. It had short limbs and four-toed feet.

- **In smaller artiodactyls**, such as sheep and goats, the foot is often divided into two parts (toes).

- **In very heavy artiodactyls**, such as hippopotamuses, there are four toes to carry the animal's weight.

- **At least two** of the middle toes on artiodactyls' feet carry an equal weight.

- **During the Miocene Epoch** (23–5 mya), artiodactyls became the most successful hoofed mammals.

- **Their success** lay more in their stomachs than in their feet. Artiodactyls evolved more advanced digestive systems, which allowed them to process the tough grasses that had replaced the earlier, softer, forest plants.

- **Another difference** between artiodactyls and perissodactyls is their ankle bones. Artiodactyls' ankle bones have more rounded joints at both ends, which means they provide more thrust when they run.

▼ Synthetoceras *had a long forked nose horn,
unlike any modern artiodactyl. However this horn
was probably present only in males.*

Entelodonts

 Entelodonts were large pig-like mammals that lived in Asia and North America in the Eocene and Miocene Epochs (56–5 mya).

 These mammals are also known as 'terminator pigs' or 'hell pigs' because of their fearsome appearance.

 One of the largest entelodonts was *Daeodon* (*Dinohyus*). It stood almost 2 m tall at the shoulder with a skull that was around one metre long.

 Daeodon **probably fed** off plant roots or scavenged for prey.

Daeodon **had** very distinctive teeth. Its incisors (front teeth) were blunt, but the teeth next to them, the canines, were sturdy and substantial, and could have been used for defence.

Another entelodont was the scavenger *Entelodon*, the largest of which was about the same size as *Daeodon*.

There are severe wounds in the fossils of some *Entelodon* skulls, such as a 2-cm-deep gash in the bone between its eyes. Palaeontologists think these were caused by the animals fighting among themselves.

Entelodon **means** 'perfect-toothed'. This mammal had a thick layer of enamel on its teeth.

However, many fossil remains of *Entelodon* have broken teeth – a result of the tough, varied diet of this scavenger.

DID YOU KNOW?

Entelodon's face had bony lumps all over it. One reason could be that they protected its eyes and nose during clashes with rivals.

▲ *The fierce-looking* Daeodon, *formerly known as* Dinohyus, *may well have scavenged for its food like modern hyenas. Its powerful neck muscles and large canine teeth suggest it could have broken bones and eaten flesh.*

Bats

- ***Icaronycteris* is one of** the earliest known bats. Its fossil remains are about 52 million years old.

- **Despite its age**, *Icaronycteris* looks very similar to a modern bat. It has a bat's typically large ears, which it probably used as a sonar, like modern bats.

- **One difference** from modern bats was that *Icaronycteris'* tail was not joined to its legs by flaps of skin.

- **Palaeontologists think** that there must have been earlier, more primitive-looking bats from which *Icaronycteris* evolved.

▲ This very rare fossil of *Icaronycteris* shows its long, strong arm or wing bones and much smaller leg bones.

▶ *The earliest bats belong to Microchiroptera mammal group. These are the smaller, insect-eating bats that are most numerous today. They are characterized by their large ears and noses, which they use during echolocation.*

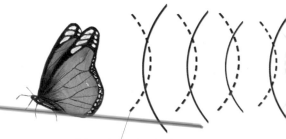

Echoes bouncing back off the butterfly

- **The chance of finding** earlier prehistoric bat fossils is very small – like birds, bats have fragile skeletons that do not fossilize well.

- *Icaronycteris* **ate insects**. Palaeontologists know this because they have found insect remains in the part of the fossil where its stomach would have been.

- *Icaronycteris* **fossils** have been found in North America.

- **The fossil remains** of another prehistoric bat, *Palaeochiropteryx*, have been found in Europe.

  - **Like *Icaronycteris***, this bat seems to have been an insectivore (insect-eater).

Sound waves
from the bat

Elephant evolution

 Elephants and their ancestors belong to an order of animals called Proboscidea, meaning 'long-snouted'. Another word for the elephant group is proboscideans.

 The first elephants appeared around 40 mya. They didn't have trunks and looked a bit like large pigs.

 Moeritherium **is one of the earliest** known animals in the elephant group. Its name comes from Lake Moeris in Egypt, where fossil-hunters discovered its remains.

 The American palaeontologist Henry Fairfield Osborn (1857–1935) described *Moeritherium* as 'a missing link' between elephants and other mammals.

 Moeritherium **was 3 m long**, weighed 200 kg, lived around 37 mya, and probably spent much of its life wallowing in rivers or shallow lakes, like a hippopotamus.

 Another stage in the development of elephants was *Phiomia*, which lived about 35 mya.

 Phiomia **had a shoulder height** of about 2.5 m. Its fossils come from North Africa and other remains found with them show it lived in swampy areas.

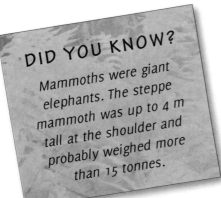

DID YOU KNOW?

Mammoths were giant elephants. The steppe mammoth was up to 4 m tall at the shoulder and probably weighed more than 15 tonnes.

🐾 **The deinotheres** were members of the elephant group, with one pair of enormous downward curving tusks in the lower jaw.

🐾 **The other groups** of the Proboscidea were the true elephants (which resembled living elephants) and the mammoths. These animals appeared in the Pliocene Epoch (5–2.5 mya).

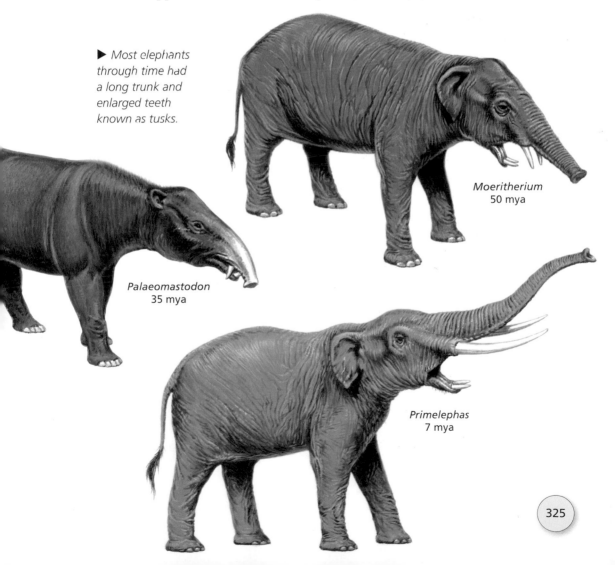

▶ *Most elephants through time had a long trunk and enlarged teeth known as tusks.*

Moeritherium
50 mya

Palaeomastodon
35 mya

Primelephas
7 mya

Woolly mammoths

- **Woolly mammoths** (scientific name *Mammuthus primigenius*) first evolved over 200,000 years ago, probably in Asia.

- **They lived on the cold grasslands** of Asia, Europe and North America, and some survived to only 4000 years ago.

- **To survive** in these cold places, woolly mammoths were designed for warmth and insulation.

- **Their woolly coats** were made up of two layers of hair – an outside layer of long, coarse hairs, and a second layer of densely packed bristles.

- **Woolly mammoths also had** very tough skins – up to 2.5 cm thick – beneath which was a deep layer of fat.

- **Male woolly mammoths** could grow up to 3.5 m long and 2.9 m high at the shoulder, and weigh up to 6 tonnes.

- **They had long tusks** that curved forward, up and then back. They used their tusks to defend themselves against attackers and probably to clear snow and ice to reach low-lying plants.

- **Some cave paintings** by ice-age humans clearly depict woolly mammoths.

- **Many excellently preserved** woolly mammoth remains have been discovered in the permanently frozen ground of Siberia.

DID YOU KNOW?

People often think the woolly mammoth had red hair, but in fact this colour was a chemical reaction that happened after the animal died.

▼ *Woolly mammoths had thick, shaggy fur to keep them warm, small ears and enormous tusks.*

Rhinoceroses

- **Rhinoceroses were a very important group** of mammals in the Paleogene and Neogene Periods (66–2.6 mya).

- *Hyracodon* **was an early rhino-like mammal** that lived in North America about 30 mya.

- **Long, slender legs** meant that *Hyracodon* would have been a fast runner. It grew to about 1.5 m long.

- **Amynodonts were a group** of prehistoric rhinos that experts believed evolved from *Hyracodon*.

- *Metamynodon* **was** an amynodont rhino-like creature. It was as large as a hippopotamus and may have had a similar lifestyle to one, wading in rivers and lakes.

- **True rhinoceroses**, the ancestors of modern rhinos, were probably descended from early versions such as *Hyracodon*.

- **One of the first true rhinos** was *Trigonias*, which had four developed toes on its front feet but three on its hind feet. It lived about 35 mya in the Late Eocene or Early Oligocene Epoch.

- *Caenopus*, **another true rhino**, had three toes on all four feet. This was the pattern for all later rhinos.

- **The largest rhinoceros** horn of all time may have belonged to *Elasmotherium*, which lived in Europe possibly up to 50,000 years ago. The horn could have been a massive 2 m long.

Rhinos became extinct in North America between 5 and 2 mya, and later in Europe. But they survived in Asia and Africa and continue to do so today, although they are severely threatened by extinction.

◄ The woolly rhino of the last great ice age died out less than 10,000 years ago.

329

Megacerops

- *Megacerops* **was formerly known** as *Brontotherium*, a large herbivore whose name means 'thunder beast'.

- **It lived in North America** and central Asia around 40–35 mya.

- *Megacerops* **was somewhere** between a rhinoceros and an elephant in size. It was 2.5 m tall at its shoulders.

- **It belonged to the group** of mammals called perissodactyls – hoofed mammals with an odd number of toes.

- *Megacerops* **had thick legs** and short, broad feet with four toes on its front feet and three toes on its hind feet.

- **On the top of its snout**, *Megacerops* had a thick, Y-shaped horn.

- **Palaeontologists think** that *Megacerops* used its horn to ward off predators and to fight rival males.

- *Megacerops* **lived in herds** on grassy plains and in forests.

- **It had big**, square molar teeth that crushed the soft leaves it fed on.

DID YOU KNOW?

Megacerops is a distant cousin of modern horses, tapirs and rhinoceroses.

▶ *Male Megacerops had larger two-pronged horns than females, which suggests that males used them for display and for fighting.*

The first horses

 Horses have one of the best fossil records of any animal. Palaeontologists have been able to trace their evolution from the earliest horse-like mammals to the modern horse.

 Hyracotherium **was an early horse**. It lived in forests in Europe in the Late Palaeocene and Early Eocene Epochs (58–50 mya).

▼ Hyracotherium *is the earliest known horse. Over time, horses became the best adapted of all hoofed animals for life on the open plains.*

- **Another name** for *Hyracotherium* used to be *Eohippus*, which means 'dawn horse', but *Eohippus* has now been given its own status as another type of early horse.

- *Hyracotherium* **was the size** of a small fox, with its head and body about 60 cm long. It had a short neck, a long tail and slender limbs. It also had three toes on its hind feet and four toes on its front feet.

- *Mesohippus* **was one of the horses** to evolve after *Hyracotherium*, between 40 and 30 mya. Its name means 'middle horse'.

- *Mesohippus* **had longer legs** than *Hyracotherium* and would have been a faster runner.

- **It would also have been better** at chewing food, because its teeth had a larger surface area.

- **An improved chewing ability** was important for horses and other plant-eaters as forests gave way to grasslands, and more abundant but tougher plants.

- *Mesohippus* **had also evolved** three toes on its front feet to match the three on its hind feet, and a longer face with elongated jaws.

- **As horses evolved**, they migrated from North America and Europe to Asia, Africa and South America.

Later horses

Merychippus, which lived between 20 and 10 mya, represented a leap forwards from earlier horses, such as *Mesohippus*. It was the size of a very small pony.

▲ Merychippus *was the biggest horse of its time, about one metre tall at the shoulders. Fossil collections suggest it lived in herds.*

Merychippus **was the first horse** to eat mainly grass, and – to help it reach the grass – it had a longer neck and muzzle (snout) than earlier horses.

Merychippus' **middle toe** had also evolved into a hoof, although this hoof did not have a pad on the bottom, unlike modern horses.

The legs of *Merychippus* were designed for outrunning carnivores. Its upper leg bones were shorter than previous horses, while the lower leg bones were longer.

Shorter upper leg bones meant that the horse's main leg-moving muscles could be packed in at the top of the leg – which translates into a faster-running animal.

Hipparion, which means 'better horse', was a further advance on *Merychippus*. It had thinner legs and more horse-like hooves. *Hipparion* lived between 20 and 1 mya.

An even more advanced horse was *Pliohippus*. The side toes that *Hipparion* still had became smaller. *Pliohippus* appeared about 5 mya.

Pliohippus' **teeth** were similar to those of modern horses – they were long and had an uneven surface for grinding up grass.

Equus, **the group that includes modern horses**, asses and zebras, is the latest stage in the evolution of the animal, first appearing around 4 mya.

335

The first whales

 The very first whales looked nothing like the enormous creatures that swim in our oceans today.

 Ambulocetus, one of the first members of the whale family, looked more like a giant otter. It lived about 50 mya.

Ambulocetus **means** 'walking whale', and it may have spent more time on land than in water.

▶ Pakicetus *could run fast and swim well. It probably lived alongside water and hunted animals both in and out of the water.*

336

Fossil remains show that *Ambulocetus* had webbed feet and hands, so it would have been a good swimmer.

 An even earlier whale ancestor than *Ambulocetus* was *Pakicetus*, which lived about 52 mya.

> *Pakicetus* **is named** after the country Pakistan, where a fossil of its skull was found in 1979.

> *Pakicetus* **was around** 1.8 m long. *Ambulocetus*, at 3 m, was bigger.

> **Palaeontologists used to think** that the whale and dolphin group, Ceracea, evolved from carnivorous hoofed mammals called mesonychids. A modern view is that the cetaceans are more closely related to the even-toed ungulates of hoofed mammals, the artiodactyls.

 Around 40 mya, the first true whales evolved from their half-walking, half-swimming ancestors. They stayed in the ocean waters and didn't come onto land.

DID YOU KNOW?
Only the back of Pakicetus' skull and part of its lower jaw have been found. However, from this, palaeontologists can tell it was not able to dive very deeply.

Later whales

 First appearing about 40 mya, *Basilosaurus* closely resembled the whales we are familiar with today, more so than its previous relatives, *Pakicetus* and *Ambulocetus*.

 It was also enormous. It measured between 20 and 25 m in length – the same as three elephants standing in a row.

Basilosaurus **had a variety of teeth** in its mouth – sharp teeth at the front for stabbing, and saw-edged teeth at the back for chewing.

These whales ate large fish, squid, and other marine mammals.

DID YOU KNOW?

Cetotherium was a prehistoric baleen whale that first appeared over 20 mya. Instead of teeth, these whales had hard plates in their mouths, called baleen, that filtered plankton and small fish.

There were some big differences between *Basilosaurus* and modern whales. For a start, it had a slimmer body.

 Basilosaurus **also lacked a blowhole**, a nostril on the top of modern whales' heads that they breathe out of when they come to the surface. Instead, it had nostrils on its snout.

▲ *The prehistoric whale* Basilosaurus, *which means 'king of the lizards', was so named because the first person to examine its remains thought it was a gigantic plesiosaur – a prehistoric marine reptile.*

 A more advanced whale than *Basilosaurus* was *Prosqualodon*. It lived between 30 and 20 mya and had a blowhole.

 Prosqualodon **may have been** similar to the ancestor of toothed whales, a group that includes sperm whales, killer whales, beaked whales and dolphins.

 Prosqualodon **looked similar** to a dolphin. It had a streamlined body about 2.5 m in length and a long, narrow snout, which was full of pointed teeth.

Early primates

 The primates are a group of mammals that include lemurs, bushbabies, tarsiers, monkeys, and apes such as gorillas, chimps and humans.

Primates have a much greater range of movement in their arms, legs, fingers and toes than other mammals.

They also have a more acute sense of touch because their fingers and toes end in flat nails, not curved claws – so the skin underneath evolved into a sensitive pad.

The ancestors of primates were small insectivorous (insect-eating) mammals that looked like shrews.

One of the first known primates was *Plesiadapis*, which lived about 57 mya in Europe and North America. It was a squirrel-like tree climber.

More advanced primates developed about 5–10 million years later. They looked a bit like modern lemurs.

Notharctus **was one** of these lemur-like primates. It ate leaves and fruit, had a head-body length of 40 cm, and a grasping thumb that would have gripped well around branches.

Other more advanced – but still early – primates include *Smilodectes* and *Cantius*. They had larger brains and eyes, longer tails and smaller snouts than *Plesiadapis*.

These animals were the early relatives of lemurs and lorises, but probably not the higher primates – the monkeys, apes and humans. Palaeontologists believe that role belongs to a different branch of primate evolution.

One early monkey was *Mesopithecus*, which lived about six mya in Greece and Turkey. It was similar to modern monkeys in many ways, but had a longer tail.

▼ *The early primate* Plesiadapis *had a long tail and claws on its fingers and toes – unlike later monkeys and apes, which had nails.*

343

Apes

- **Apes are primates** that have more complex brains than monkeys and no tails. They include lesser and great apes and humans.

- *Aegyptopithecus* was one of the early pre-apes. It lived in Egypt in the Oligocene Epoch (34–23 mya). It was small and had a short tail.

- **An early ape** that lived between 25 and 23 mya was *Proconsul*. Its body size varied from that of a small monkey to that of a female gorilla, and it had a larger brain than *Aegyptopithecus*.

▼ The early ape Dryopithecus *stood about one metre tall. It had the largest brain for its size of any mammal at the time, and it flourished in open grassland regions in Africa, Asia and Europe.*

Proconsul **was a fruit-eater**. Palaeontologists think that it walked on four limbs with part of its weight supported by the knuckles of its hands, like modern chimpanzees and gorillas.

 Several lines of apes developed after *Proconsul*. They led to lesser apes or gibbons, the Asian great apes the orang-utans, and the African great apes, the chimpanzees, gorillas and humans.

 Dryopithecus **was a chimp-like ape** that evolved after *Proconsul* and lived in the Late Miocene Epoch (15–5 mya). It may have stood on two legs but climbed using all four.

Sivapithecus **was an ape** that lived from about 12 to 8 mya. It is now thought to be part of the chain of evolution of Asian apes and is possibly an ancestor of the orang-utan. It was once also called *Ramapithecus*.

Australopithecines were a further step in the evolution from apes to humans. Australopithecines (meaning 'southern apes') were found in Africa and some walked on two legs.

The biggest ape was *Gigantopithecus*, which lived in China from about 8 to less than 1 mya. It may have been up to 2.5 m tall and weighed 300 kg.

Ardipithecus

- **A possible early hominin** (humans and close relatives) was *Ardipithecus ramidus*, which lived about 4.5 mya.

- **It would have looked similar** to a chimpanzee in many ways, except for one major difference – *Ardipithecus ramidus* could walk on two legs.

- **It probably lived** in woods and forests, sleeping in trees at night, but foraging on the ground for roots during the day.

- **A full-grown** *Ardipithecus ramidus* was about 1.3 m tall and weighed up to 50 kg.

- **Archaeologists discovered** the teeth, skull and arm bone fossils of *Ardipithecus ramidus* in Ethiopia and it was named in 1994.

- **In 2001**, archaeologists in Ethiopia found the remains of an even older hominid, *Ardipithecus kadabba*, which lived between 5.6 and 5.8 mya.

- **The fossils** of *Ardipithecus kadabba* are similar to those of *Ardipithecus ramidus*, so it is possible they are very closely related.

- **The name** *kadabba* comes from the local language version of 'basal family ancestor'.

- *Australopithecus anamensis* is a later hominin than *Ardipithecus ramidus*. Its fossils date to between 4.2 and 3.9 million years old.

- **A fossil** of one of *Australopithecus anamensis'* knee-joints shows that it shifted its weight from one leg to the other when it moved – a sure sign that it walked on two legs.

▲ Ardipithecus ramidus. *Scientists chose its name from the Afar language of Ethiopia –* ardi *means 'ground' while* ramid *means 'root' – words that express its position at the base of human history.*

347

Australopithecus africanus

🦶 **Australopithecus africanus**, which means 'the southern ape of Africa', was an early hominid that emerged between 3 and 2 mya.

🦶 **This species** was the first australopithecine to be discovered.

🦶 **The Australian-born** scientist Raymond Dart made the discovery of this important fossil in South Africa in 1924.

▼ *This reconstruction of* Australopithecus africanus *shows a projecting ape-like jaw but also a forehead that does not slope back so much as in modern apes.*

- **The fossil** that Dart identified was found in a quarry near the village of Taung, on the edge of the Kalahari Desert.

- **It was the fossil** of a skull, belonging to a child around two or three years old. The fossil became known as the Taung child.

- **Many people** did not believe in Dart's discovery – they thought it was an ape, not a hominin. But one person did believe it – the archaeologist Robert Broom.

- **In 1947**, Broom himself found a skull of an adult *Australopithecus africanus*.

- **The adult skull** became known as 'Mrs Ples' because Broom first thought it belonged to a different species, *Plesianthropus transvaalensis*.

- **By the 1950s** other parts of *Australopithecus africanus*' skeleton had been unearthed, including a pelvis and a femur.

- **These fossils proved** beyond doubt that *Australopithecus africanus* was an upright-walking hominin.

DID YOU KNOW?

'Hominid' is used to refer to modern and extinct Great Apes and all their immediate ancestors. 'Hominin' is used to refer to modern and extinct humans and all their immediate ancestors.

Homo habilis

- *Homo habilis* is one of the earliest known members of the genus *Homo*, to which we also belong. It lived between 2.3 and 1.4 mya.

- **The archaeologists** Louis and Mary Leakey first discovered its remains at Olduvai Gorge in Tanzania, in 1960–61.

- **Fossils of *Homo habilis*** skulls have since been found around Lake Turkana in Kenya, one of the richest sites for hominid fossils in the world.

- **The skulls show** that *Homo habilis* had a flat face with prominent cheekbones, similar to australopithecines, which it would have lived alongside.

▲ *The first* Homo habilis *skull found by Louis and Mary Leakey in Tanzania. It had a bigger brain than any previous hominin.*

- *Homo habilis* was much more ape-like than its successors, such as *Homo ergaster*. It probably had body fur and lacked any form of language.

- **But it did have a bigger brain** than any australopithecine. It also had more flexible hands and straighter, more sensitive fingers.

Homo habilis means 'handy man'
– it could use its hands to gather
fruit and it also created stone
tools, known as Oldowan.

A fully grown Homo habilis
male was around 1.4 m tall and
weighed about 50 kg.

▶ Homo habilis *showed the trend of
jaws that protruded less compared
to earlier relatives.*

DID YOU KNOW?
Homo habilis used stone
tools to crack open animal
bones so it could eat the
nutritious marrow inside.

Homo erectus

- **About 1.8 million years ago** a new form of human appeared in Africa – *Homo erectus*. Some scientists think that a similar form, *Homo ergaster*, may have been a type of *Homo erectus*.

- **The body of *Homo erectus*** was very similar to that of a modern human, and was also tall, with some specimens standing 1.8 m in height.

- **The head was rather different** to that of modern humans, having a heavy ridge of bone over the eyes and protruding jaws that made it look more ape-like.

- **Some remains indicate** that *Homo erectus* was capable of building huts out of wood and brushwood. These were probably temporary shelters for a tribe on the move, not permanent homes.

- *Homo erectus* spread beyond Africa and settled in Europe and Asia.

DID YOU KNOW?

The 'Peking Man' fossils disappeared at the beginning of World War II and have never been found. They were confiscated by Japanese troops just when they were about to be shipped to the USA.

- **In the late 19th century**, Eugène Dubois discovered *Homo erectus* fossils on the Indonesian island of Java. At the time he named them *Pithecanthropus erectus*, which later changed to *Homo erectus*.

- **In the 1930s**, archaeologists found over 40 *Homo erectus* skeletons in China, naming them *Sinanthropus pekinensis*.

For a long time, people called the human to which the Chinese fossils belonged 'Peking Man'. It was much later that palaeoanthropologists realized it was in fact *Homo erectus*.

 Archaeologists have also found evidence that *Homo erectus* used fire and practised cannibalism.

▼ *Stone hearths that were used by* Homo erectus *prove that it had mastered fire. Fire provided warmth, light, protection and the means to cook food.*

Homo neanderthalensis

- *Homo neanderthalensis* – or Neanderthals – lived between around 300,000 and perhaps 30,000 years ago across Europe, West Asia and parts of the Middle East.

- **The name** *Homo neanderthalensis* means 'man from the Neander Valley', which is the site in Germany where the first of its fossil remains were found in 1865.

- **Neanderthals are our extinct cousins** rather than our direct ancestors – they are from a different branch of the human family.

- **They were about 30 percent heavier** than modern humans. Their bodies were more sturdy and they had shorter legs.

- **Neanderthals' shorter, stockier bodies** were better suited than modern humans to life in Europe, West Asia and parts of the Middle East during the ice ages of the Pleistocene Epoch (2.6 million to 12,000 years ago).

- **Their faces** were also different, with sloping foreheads and heavy brow ridges.

- **They buried their dead**, cooked meat and made various tools and weapons.

- **Neanderthals made** the first ever spears tipped with stone blades.

> ▶ *Neanderthals showed great skills in hunting, collecting plants and cooking foods.*

DID YOU KNOW?

Many people think that Neanderthals were slow and stupid, but in fact their brains were at least as big as modern humans' brains.

Modern humans

 All people alive today are (anatomically) modern humans, subspecies *Homo sapiens sapiens*.

Various evidence suggests when and where modern humans appeared, including tools, fossil bones and teeth, genetic material (DNA) extracted from them, and genes from living people.

Most evidence shows modern humans appeared around 200,000 years ago in East Africa.

The oldest fossils recognized as modern humans come from Omo, in Ethiopia, dated to 195,000 years ago.

By 90,000 years ago, modern humans had become established in Africa and started to spread into the Middle East. This migration is known as 'Out of Africa'.

From the Middle East, modern humans spread into Europe by 40,000 years ago as 'Cro-Magnon People'.

 They also spread east into Asia, South East Asia and then Australia by 45,000 years ago.

 Other modern humans spread north-east through Asia into north-west North America by 15,000 years ago, and then south through the Americas.

As modern humans spread, they replaced archaic *Homo sapiens* and other humans living in each region.

However modern humans may have interbred with some of these other groups, such as the Neanderthals in Europe.

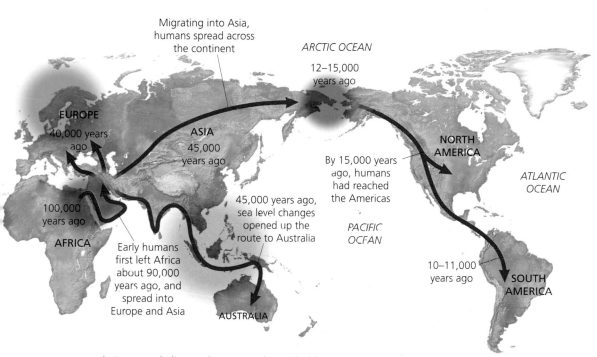

Migrating into Asia,
humans spread across
the continent

ARCTIC OCEAN

12–15,000
years ago

EUROPE
40,000 years
ago

ASIA
45,000
years ago

NORTH
AMERICA

By 15,000 years
ago, humans
had reached
the Americas

ATLANTIC
OCEAN

100,000
years ago

45,000 years ago,
sea level changes
opened up the
route to Australia

PACIFIC
OCEAN

AFRICA

Early humans
first left Africa
about 90,000
years ago, and
spread into
Europe and Asia

10–11,000
years ago

SOUTH
AMERICA

AUSTRALIA

▲ *Improved climate (green area) enabled humans to migrate into Europe and Asia from Africa. Changes in the sea level (orange area) opened up the route to Australia. Ice age glaciations (blue areas) limited migration north and east, but once established, the Americas were swiftly populated.*

Modern humans gradually adapted to the climate and other conditions in each region, producing the variety of people around the world today.

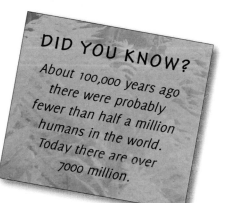

DID YOU KNOW?

About 100,000 years ago there were probably fewer than half a million humans in the world. Today there are over 7000 million.

Brains and intelligence

- **Primates, including all the various** kinds of humans, had bigger brains in relation to their body size than other mammals.

- **Primates developed** larger brains – and more intelligence – because living in and moving between trees required a high degree of balance, coordination and the skilful use of hands and feet.

- **Once hominids' brains** started getting bigger, so their skulls began to change. Bigger brains led to the development of foreheads.

- *Homo habilis'* **brain** was 50 percent bigger than its australopithecine predecessors. It had a brain capacity of 750 cubic cm.

- **The structure of its brain** was different to that of earlier hominids. It had much bigger frontal lobes – the parts of the brain associated with planning and problem-solving.

Australopithecus afarensis

Homo habilis

Homo habilis put its greater intelligence to use in the quest to find meat, which it scavenged from other animals' kills to supplement its diet.

 Eating more meat allowed hominids' brains to get even bigger. Breaking down plant food uses up a huge amount of energy, so the fewer plants hominids ate, the more energy was available for their brains.

Homo ergaster had an even bigger brain, with a capacity of around 1000 cubic cm. It could use this intelligence to read tracks left by animals – a major development in hunting.

The brain of *Homo erectus* became larger during its existence. About one mya its brain capacity was 1000 cubic cm, 500,000 years later it was 1300 cubic cm.

The average human brain capacity today is 1350–1450 cubic cm.

Homo sapiens

◀ *Brain size is linked to intelligence, but size isn't everything. What makes humans and our ancestors intelligent is our brain's complex structure.*

Language

Language may go back as far as *Homo erectus* or *Homo ergaster* – although this would probably have been a much simpler form of communication than we use today.

One reason for language development was as a way of maintaining relationships within groups.

Language is different from cries of alarm or mating calls. It involves a system for representing ideas and feelings.

An important feature in speech is the pharynx – a tube in the neck, from the vocal cords (contained in the larynx) to the mouth.

In other primates the pharynx is too short to produce complex modifications of sound.

Homo erectus/ergaster probably had a longer pharynx than earlier hominins, suggesting it was able to produce basic speech.

Chimpanzee

Pharynx

Tongue

Homo heidelbergensis had an even longer pharynx and would have been able to produce complex sounds. However, its speech would have differed from ours because of the different shape of its face.

Neanderthals would also have been able to speak. The fossil remains of a Neanderthal hyoid bone, which supports the larynx, is almost identical to a modern human's.

Modern speech probably only developed with the arrival of *Homo sapiens sapiens*.

Some experts think that modern speech first developed around 150,000 years ago – others think it did not happen until less than 50,000 years ago.

Human

Pharynx

Tongue

◄ The physical differences between a chimpanzee (far left) and a modern human (left) mean that the human is capable of speech, but the chimpanzee is not. Unlike chimpanzees and early hominins, modern humans have long throats and shorter muzzles. Therefore our pharynxes can produce a range of sounds and our tongues can move backwards and forwards in our mouths to utter these sounds.

Tools

▲ Homo habilis *produced flakes of stone, such as this one, by striking one stone against another, called a hammerstone.*

- **The greatest number** of *Homo habilis* tools has been found in the Olduvai Gorge in Tanzania. They include rocks that were used as hammers, flakers, choppers and scrapers.

- *Homo habilis* used these tools to cut meat and, especially, to scrape open animal bones to eat the marrow inside.

- **The stone tools** used by *Homo habilis* are crude and basic. This hominin was one of the the first tool-makers, but not a skilled one as yet.

- **Making these early stone tools** was still a challenging task – the tool-maker needed to strike one rock with another so that it would produce a single, sharp flake rather than shattering into many pieces.

◀ Homo erectus *used hammers made of bone to produce thinner and sharper flakes of stone.*

Tool-making requires considerable intelligence. It involves the use of memory, as well as the ability to plan ahead and to solve abstract problems.

 Homo erectus' **tools** were more advanced. This hominin made tear-drop shaped, symmetrical hand axes called Acheulean axes, after the place in France where similar axes have been discovered from a later period.

 Neanderthals developed a method for producing razor-sharp flakes of stone, called Levallois flakes, which could be placed on the end of spears.

This method required great precision and dexterity. While modern humans have a much broader range of skills, most would be very hard pushed to produce such tools themselves.

 Modern humans developed the greatest variety of tools. Cro-Magnon tools include knives, spearpoints and engraving tools.

Cro-Magnon humans also began to make tools from materials other than stone, including wood, bones, antlers and ivory.

▲ Homo sapiens' *tools became more and more complex.
They incorporated different materials, such as twine in the axe
(top) and flint teeth held in place by resin in this saw (bottom).*

Hunting

- **One of the earliest** human hunters was *Homo erectus*. Other hominins that came before it, like *Homo habilis*, may have hunted small or lame animals, but probably they mostly scavenged other animals' kills.

- *Homo erectus* used fire to drive animals into traps. They also developed handaxes, which they used to kill animals or butcher them once they were dead.

- **In the 1990s,** finds of *Homo heidelbergensis* weapons in Boxgrove, England, showed the complete range of this species' hunting arsenal. It included axes, slicing knives, and blades for cutting and slashing.

- **A site at Schöningen, Germany**, preserved the remains of several polished wooden spears of spruce wood, probably made by *Homo heidelbergensis*.

- **Each of these spears** was over 2 m long, and was designed to be thrown like a javelin.

- **Hunting developed** into a way of providing not only food, but also clothing (animal skins) and materials for tools (bones, horns and hooves).

- **It was the Neanderthals** that excelled in hunting – a skill they developed during the ice ages of the Pleistocene Epoch (2.6–0.01 mya).

- **Neanderthals used nets** or spears to catch spawning fish. They also hunted seals by spearing them through holes in the ice or by throwing spears at them.

As well as hunting for meat, hominins also gathered wild fruits, vegetables and nuts.

Homo sapiens developed new weapons for hunting, including the bow and arrow, the blowpipe and the boomerang.

▼ *Various kinds of evidence show Neanderthal people hunted animals, lived in rock shelters, and held ceremonies to bury their dead.*

Cave art

- **Cro-Magnon people** produced many cave paintings.

- **One of the best examples** is the Grotte de Chauvet in the Ardeche, France, which was discovered in 1994.

- **The Grotte de Chauvet** caves contain more than 300 drawings of animals, from lions and deer to buffalos and woolly rhinoceroses.

- **People used to be very sceptical** that early humans could have produced cave paintings and thought they were hoaxes.

- **Another magnificent example** of cave painting is that of the Altamira cave in northern Spain, which has an 18-m-long ceiling covered with red-, black- and violet-coloured paintings of bison.

- **Most cave paintings** date from around 30,000 to 15,000 years ago, when Cro-Magnon man lived in Europe and elsewhere.

- **Other cave paintings** may be much older. Some archaeologists think that the Cave of El Castillo paintings in Spain are 40,000 years old.

- **Many cave pictures** appear to represent hunting scenes, but there are also many symbols in caves, including patterns of squares and dots.

- **Another very common image** in caves is that of a human hand.

DID YOU KNOW?

Cro-Magnon people made hand outlines by blowing a sooty pigment over their hand as they pressed it against the cave wall.

▶ A series of cave paintings known as the Great Hall of Bulls in Lascaux, southwest France. The paintings are around 17,000 years old.

Index

Index

Entries in **bold** refer to main entries; entries in *italics* refer to illustrations.

Acknowledgements

All artworks are from the Miles Kelly Artwork Bank.

The publishers would like to thank the following sources for the use of their photographs:
Alamy 160 Stocktrek Images, Inc.; 164 MasPix; 270 Ronald Karpilo; 314 Stocktrek Images, Inc.
Getty 154 Roman Garcia Mora/Stocktrek Images; 202 Eric Préau; 230 Roman Garcia Mora/Stocktrek Images; 234 James L. Amos; 244 Sergey Krasovskiy/Stocktrek Images; 246 Dinos; 304 Daniel Eskridge/Stocktrek Images; 348 Régis Bossu; 366 Philippe Wojazer **Glow Images** 134 Superstock; 350 Superstock **National Geographic Creative** 222 Matthias Breiter/Minden Pictures; 223 Pete Oxford/Minden Pictures; 254 Lowell Georgi; 292 Jonathon Blair; 294 Adrie and Alfons Kennis **Science Photo Library** 60–66 Jaime Chirinos; 84 De Agostini/UIG; 136 Mark Hallett PaleoArt; 180 Millard H. Sharp; 198 Laurie O'Keefe; 216 Laurie O'Keefe; 220 Natural History Museum, London; 226 History Museum, London; 280–284 Jaime Chirinos; 286 Walter Myers; 290 Jaime Chirinos; 296 Mauricio Anton; 306 Mark Hallett PaleoArt; 310–312 Natural History Museum, London; 338 Natural History Museum, London; 354 Mauricio Anton; 356 Claus Lunau; 364 Christian Jegou Publiphoto Diffusion **Shutterstock.com** 10 BMJ; 14 BergelmLicht; 70 Michael Rosskothen; 74 Michael Rosskothen; 86 leonello calvetti; 88 Jean-Michel Girard; 96 Catmando; 104 Linda Bucklin; 106 Kostyantyn Ivanyshen; 108 Linda Bucklin; 112 Linda Bucklin; 116–118 Linda Bucklin; 120 Catmando; 132 Linda Bucklin; 138 Catmando; 142 Michael Rosskothen; 144 Catmando; 150 Bob Orsillo; 152 Catmando; 156 Ralf Juergen Kraft; 160–170 Linda Bucklin; 176–178 leonello calvetti; 186 Ozja; 188 Jean-Michel Girard; 190 ags1973; 196 DM7; 206 Linda Bucklin; 210 Linda Bucklin; 217 John Kasawa; 218 leonello calvetti; 236 DM7; 238 Naypong; 252 Michael Rosskothen; 258 Bob Orsillo; 264 troyka; 265 Trevor kelly; 276 Catmando; 288 Rich Koele; 298 Ralf Juergen Kraft; 308 Ralf Juergen Kraft; 320 Ralf Juergen Kraft; 326 Ozja; 330 Catmando; 340 Procy **Superstock** 9 Science Picture Co; 26 Stocktrek Images

Every effort has been made to acknowledge the source and copyright holder of each picture. Miles Kelly Publishing apologizes for any unintentional errors or omissions.